PROFILE OF THE AUTHOR

Professor Li Ding was born in Henan Province in China on October 10th, 1935. He graduated in 1960 from Shanxi Medical College, where he secured a teaching job. He continued his studies in the physics department of Tianjin's Nankai University. He is now a director of the All-China Association of Acupuncture and Moxibustion, vice-secretary general of the Shanxi Society of Acupuncture and Moxibustion, vice-chairman of the Shanxi International Training Centre for Acupuncture and Massage, an executive member of the Shanxi Research Association of Qigong and president of the Qigong Society of Shanxi Medical College, where he is a professor. He is honorary chairman of the Sino-Japanese Qigong Health Care Centre and has lectured as a visiting professor at the Kui Qigong Research Academy in Milan and the Academy of Natural Therapy in Singapore.

For the last 30 years he has written and compiled many books on traditional Chinese medicine and materia medica, acupuncture and Qigong and has also published treatises. As a positive supporter of traditional Chinese medicine as a main approach to disease treatment and prevention supplemented by Western medicine, he has trained dozens of acupuncturists from more than 20 countries in the last few years. His "Jianmei Jingluo Tu" and "Fourteen Meridians" have been released in more than 50 countries. He was awarded in 1985 the All-China May Day Worker's Medal and National Outstanding Scientific Worker Certificate. He also bears the title of Excellent Teacher from the Shanxi Medicine College. He was cited again in 1986 by Shanxi Province for his fruitful research. The "Dictionary of Acupuncture Points" he compiled in June 1986 has been published by the Tokyo Academic Publishing House in Japan, where it was praised as an "epoch-making book on the subject".

He came out with "Meridian Qigong" in July 1985 and has trained a lot of Meridian Qigong learners from Singapore, Germany, America, England, Belgium, Norway and India. His Meridian Qigong has been called the newest type of transmission of Qi along meridians to treat disease and keep fit and a Qigong that teaches Chinese medicine, acupuncture and the maintainance of health. On the basis of 18 Moves from Taiji Qigong, he and Mr Bambang Sutomo developed a Taiji Qigong in 28 moves and published a book in 1986. He has been invited to lecture in Italy and twice in Singapore.

He is currently engaged in international academic and non-official exchanges and the study of historical records, as well as teaching, clinical work and scientific research.

ABOUT THE AUTHOR

Mr Chen Zhongxing, alias Bambang Sutomo, is an Indonesian Chinese born in Fak Fak, Indonesia on November 17, 1937. Presently he is general manager and director of the Indonesian International Import and Export Company, founder and chairman of the Indonesian Taiji Qigong Centre Foundation, chairman of the Southeast Asian Scientific Academy for Qigong Health Care and a prime mover in the International Qigong Science Association. He has taught Qigong free for many years, having as many as 330,000 students, 220,000 in Indonesia and the rest in Singapore, Malaysia, the Philippines, Thailand, Mainland China and Taibei, Japan, the U.S., Australia and Italy. For his contribution the Indonesian Government awarded him a certificate of merit on February 29, 1988.

Mr Chen advocates active physical training and Qigong practice for all in the pursuit of health and longevity and to enhance mental and visceral functioning in order to contribute more to man's wisdom and development.

He has cooperated with Professor Li Ding in the study and revision of 28-move Taiji Qigong since 1987. He and others set up a preliminary committee for the International Qigong Science Association in Singapore, an organization of outstanding Qigong and Gongfu masters and scientists from China (including Taibei), Indonesia, Singapore, Japan, Malaysia, the U.S., France, Argentina, West Germany, Hongkong and Switzerland.

He is editor of the Oriental Traditional Medicine and Medical Care Committee founded at his instigation in May, 1985. As a devotee to the discovery and systematization of Oriental traditional medicine and health care, he has forwarded cultural and non-official exchanges between the East and West and contributed to the United Nations goal of medical care for all by 2000.

ABOUT THE TRANSLATOR

Mr. Flingoh C. H. Oh is a senior research officer with the Palm Oil Research Institute of Malaysia. He graduated in Physics with a B. Sc. Hons. degree and obtained his M. Sc. degree in Chemistry. Born in 1947 he is a member of the Chinese Medical Association of Malaysia. He studied Chinese medicine in Kuala Lumpur, Singapore and Hong Kong and has undergone training under various masters including raw herbal medicine from his late father. He also studied reflexology in Scotland.

He learned various types of Qigong, including the Taiji Qigong Twenty-Eight Steps from Professor Li Ding personally while Professor Li was in Singapore on different occasions.

In his spare time he practises Chinese medicine since 1965 while he was still a student in high school. He treats various illnesses by acupuncture, acupressure, massage, reflexology and natural therapy including Qigong, physical exercises and yoga. One of the special problems he treats is baldness and hair loss.

FOREWORD

Taiji Qigong Twenty-Eight Steps was compiled and written basing on the *Taiji Qigong Eighteen Steps*, taking into consideration the activities of both parts of the cerebrum and also combining the meridian theory of traditional Chinese medicine. After studying the Taiji Qigong Eighteen Steps from Dr. Chan Kwei-Lan of Harbin, I felt this is a very good system and is very easy to promote widely. However, if some of the steps were modified into both left and right procedures and if some more steps were added then the system will be nearer to perfection. So I have compiled and written this form of *Taiji Qigong Twenty-Eight Steps*. During the compilation and writing, I present each step in three parts, i.e. theory, method and functions. My approach is based on the harmony of heart (mind), breathing and energy during the practice of each step while I give special emphasis on the inner will and concentration (Yi Nian) or a combination of both inner and outer Yi Nian but with emphasis on the former.

During the year of 1987, I presented my findings first in Italy and then in Singapore during academic conferences and these have been well received by Taiji Qigong experts because it is a therapeutic, health promoting and life nurturing method. It is easy to learn, easy to practise, it improves health and prevents illness. If one practises Taiji Qigong Twenty-Eight Steps after learning the Taiji Qigong Eighteen Steps, then it will further improve the effects and usefulness of the practice and also give a better understanding of the theory of meridians and the internal organs of the Oriental Medicine, bringing one to a higher level of understanding and results.

In May, 1988, I with Mr. Bambang Sutomo, Founder and President of Indonesia Taiji Qigong Centre Foundation, and President of Southeast Asian Qigong Scientific Research Institute, revised the manuscript again. The manuscript has been translated into English by Dr. Flingoh C. H. Oh. The book also will be published in Chinese, Japanese, French and Indonesian. Here I wish to thank the followings for their support and development of the Taiji Qigong Twenty-Eight Steps:

Old Grand Master Li Tze Ming of Beijing; Mr. Pei Xi Ron of Shanghai; Dott. Cho-Hwa Chen of Universita Di Pavia, Milan; Dr. Kasenda of West Germany; Dr. Martino of Cancer Research Institute, Milan; Mr. Ou Ker Bin Ti of Milan Kwei Taiji Qigong Center; Mr. T. T Ang, President of Singapore Acupuncture Society and Principal of Chinese Nature-Cure Institute, Singapore; Mr. Phang Siao Chong, Secretary of Singapore Acupuncture Society; Mr. Bambang Sutomo, President of Indonesia Taiji Qigong Association; Mr. Chan Kai Sam, President of Penang Hur Shaing Chuan Breathing and Physical Health Center; Dr. Kimbei Sato, President of Chinese Martial Art Alliance All-of Japan; Reverend Jiang of Reverend Jiang Qigong Institute, Hong Kong-Malaysia; and Mr. Flingoh C. H. Oh, Senior Research Officer of Palm Oil Research Institute of Malaysia.

Professor Li Ding
Shanxi Medical College
China
17 March, 1988

CONTENTS

I. HOW TO DO WELL IN TAIJI QIGONG TWENTY-EIGHT STEPS

Taiji Qigong Twenty-Eight Steps has the advantages of both the Taiji Quan and Qigong. It has firmness and gentleness, fullness with emptiness, peace and tranquillity while in motion, unbroken continuity in the steps, soft and harmonious movements, and combination of will (Yi), vital force (Qi) and spirit (Shen). It is a popular inner health cultivation method which combines both movements and tranquillity. Beginners should note these points:

1. You need to manage to the breathing rhythm well. Breathing need to be deep, long, slow, fine and even. In these ways the red blood cells in the body can carry more oxygen to nourish all the other cells in the body, particularly the grain cells and the cells in all the five solid-Zang organs and six hollow-Fu organs* providing a good material foundation for the psysiological functions of the body.

2. You should understand the theory, method and functions of each step. In your movement, you need to coordinate hands and feet, elbows and knees, shoulders and hips and these are known as the three co-ordinations. Correct and harmonious movements are the requirements for doing well in the system.

3. During the practice of the Qigong, emphasis should be given to the inner concentration. The ability to convert the external concentration into the inner

concentration is an important factor for successful practice of this Qigong.

The term "inner concentration" here refers to the flow of thought that regulates and protects the cerebrum, through the transmission or guarding of the flow of thought, to manifest the function of Qi and to set the motion of life in body. If you can not calm the concentration down, then you often would not achieve the aims of the practice.

II. SELF-EVALUATION OF THE EFFECTS AFTER PRACTISING

With long term consistent practice, the effect of this Qigong may be evaluated in the following aspects: If you have any illness before practising, it is better to have a full examination done in the hospital and keep the records of all the abnormal results. You may evaluate after every 3—6 months of practice and you will know the effects of practising the Qigong. Normally with consistent practice you will feel the results as outlined below:

1. Head
After practising—The head feels clear, the body feels light and comfortable, the memory power increases, sleep better, more alert, faster thinking and more

---

*The five Zang and six Fu refer to the various internal organs of the body. For a more detail discussion, please see Note 11-1 in Step 11 (From the translator).

energetic. These effects are brought by sufficient supply of oxygen to the brain cells and all the other cells in the body.

2. Eyes

After practising and with the increase in oxygen supply and improvement in the blood circulation—The "eyes can see better with better supplies of blood", the heart is tranquil (peaceful mind), eyes are bright and vision is clearer.

3. Heart and Lungs

With consistent practice—Improved functions of the heart and lungs, increased heart contraction power, no dysphoria and short of breath, and usually better ECG.

4. Chest

With consistent practice—More cheerful abundant pectoral Qi (Zongqi)* in the chest, forceful and loud voice, smooth and comfortable breathing.

5. Spleen and Stomach

With consistent practice—Better appetite and improvement in "nourishment of the acquired nutrients".

6. Liver and Gall Bladder

With consistent practice—Improved functions of liver and gall bladder thus promoting the digestive and absorption functions, increasing the body resistance and immunity to diseases. Those who often suffer from cold and flu, the occurrence may be prevented or reduced.

7. Abdomen
With consistent practice—Reduce the fat deposit, enhance the peristaltic movements of stomach and intestines, makes you look better and prevent the increase of blood cholesterol content.

8. Reproduction
With consistent practice—Increased reproductive ability and also prevention of nocturnal emission, impotence, menoxenia and prostatitis.

9. The Four Limbs
With consistent practice—Smooth and active joints of the four limbs, strengthened tendons and bones, firm and fast movements.

10. Spine
With consistent practice—Smooth and free movement of spine, prevention of hunchback and deformation.

---

*Pectoral Qi (Zongqi): Clean Qi (Qingqi) and Qi from essence of food, obtained respectively from the atmosphere and food after birth, are known as acquired Qi. The two kinds of Qi meet in the chest forming essential Qi (Zongqi).

TAIJI QIGONG TWENTY-EIGHT STEPS

THE FIRST PART:
from step 1 to 10

STEP 1: BEGINNING STEP AND REGULATING BREATHING

THEORY:

"Beginning" refers to the starting posture of the practice; "regulating breathing" means regulating the breathing rhythm. "Breathing" here refers to the complete cycle of inhale and exhale movements. This is a very important step and in practising this step two points should be remembered. These are "relax and tranquil". "Relax" requires that the whole body is relaxing and not tense, and the movement is similar to the beginning movement of Taiji Quan (both feet parallel, shoulder width, sink the shoulders, fall the elbows, body upright and relax, picture supporting a light object on the head and fingers slightly curved); "tranquil" means peace at heart (in mind). The Heart Meridian enters the brain through the eyes, and the heart is commanding the blood; the heart and the mind are interconnected, hence it is said the heart keeps the spirit, i.e. once the brain is "tranquil", then the "spirit" is at "peace". To get rid of the other thoughts, the eyes should be half close and half open, this will prevent the external interferences from the environment and people, reaching a state of look but not see, like clear but not clear, like sleeping but not sleeping, and forgetting oneself. This is the state for practising the Qigong. When the whole body is "relax" and the mind is "tranquil", this will result in a protective control of the mind and improve the activities of all functions under the control of the cerebrum. With deep, slow, long, fine and even breathing, the oxygen content of the blood is increased and this results in improving the oxygen supplies to the cerebrum, heart, kidney, liver, spleen, lungs and other organs, resulting in betterment of their important physiological functions.

After standing "relax and tranquil" and fully "peaceful" you should take care of the direction of concentration,* and you should have the control of concentration, Qi and energy, and in here it lies an important difference between Qigong and normal physical exercises.

This step calls for inner concentration, beginning from Dantian** (extra) to Shanzhong*** (Ren 17) and then branches to the Laogong**** (P 8) of the palms,

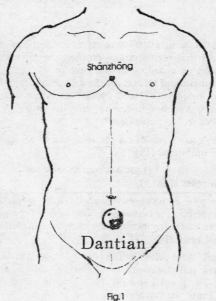

Fig. 1

after this the concentration is always in the Laogong (P 8) during the raising and lowering movements.

METHOD:

1. Standing relax and tranquil, relax the whole body, both feet parallel in shoulder width, concentration (Note 1-1) raises from Dantian (extra) goes up to Shanzhong (Ren 17), branching out to both Laogong (P 8), both arms gradually raise forward till horizontal, palms***** (Note 1-2) facing down, concentration on Laogong (P 8), accompanied by slow inhalation (Figs. 1-1, 1-2).

---

*The term "concentration" here refers to "Yi Nian" which is the flow of thought that regulates and protects the cerebrum. Through the transmission or guarding of the flow of thought, one aims to manifest the function of Qi and set the motion of life in body, mind, breathing and energy. "Yi" and "Nian" literally mean "will" and "thought" respectively and in combination the term may be translated as equivalent to "concentration".

**Dantian (extra) locates on the mid-line of the abdomen 1.5-4 *cun* below the umbilicus (Fig. 1).

***Shanzhong (Ren 17) locates on the mid-line of the sternum, between the nipples (Fig. 1).

****Laogong (P 8) location: When the hand is placed with the palm upward the point is between the 2nd and 3rd metacarpal bones proximal to the metacarpophalangeal joint, on the radial side of the 3rd metacarpal bone (Fig. 2).

*****"Palms" here refers to the center (hollow) of the palm and unless otherwise stated it does not refer to the back (volardorsal side) of the palms. The point Laogong (P 8) is some where at the center of the palm (From the translator).

8

Fig.2

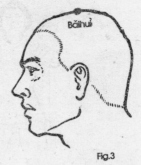

Fig.3

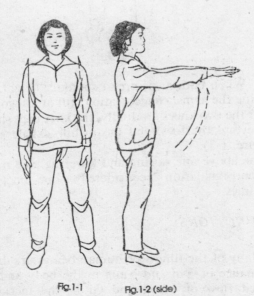

Fig.1-1   Fig.1-2 (side)

Fig.1-3

2. When both arms are at shoulder height, without moving the arms, concentration still at Laogong (P 8), lower the two knees gradually, the knee caps should not go beyond the toes, and meanwhile exhale gradually (Figure. 1-3).

The above one raising and lowering, one inhalation and one exhalation is considered as one time, repeat 3—5 times.

FUNCTIONS:

Many of the illness of human beings are due to the imbalance of Yin and Yang in the body and the disturbed flow of blood and Qi in the meridians. In common terms these mean that the cerebrum is subjected to various external and internal unfavorable stimulations resulting in the imbalance of the body functions. Hence at the beginning of the practice, one should concentrate to get rid of the undesirable thoughts, protect the cerebrum and at the same time regulate the breathing to increase oxygen content in the blood. These are very important in improving the functions of the cerebrum and other important organs. The gradual lowering of the knee will produce the feeling that the practice has already begun.

This step is useful in adjusting the function of the cerebrum, suppressing and eliminating various latent chronic illness of the cerebrum, resulting in the peace of mind and also in lubricating and smoothening the joints.

STEP 2: OPENING UP YOUR CHEST

THEORY:

"Opening Up" here means to open and expand into large space and no more in closed situation. In addition, the movement of this step makes the chest cavity expands and obviously increases the breathing functions, effectively increases the oxygen content of the blood. Hence the name of "opening up your chest". Once the practice starts, and after calming down, then with bigger deep breathing, the oxygen content in the body is increased. This means that the cerebrum receives more oxygen and becomes clear and alert, the chest receives more oxygen and opens up, giving rise to a feeling of joy, confidence, alertness and quick think-

Fig.2-1

ing.

This step needs the hands to assist the concentration, use the concentration to lead the Qi, and breathing in deep, long, slow and even rhythms. The concentration is at Laogong (P. 8), in the middle of the palms.

METHOD:

1. From the previous step, when the body changes from the lowered to the up-right position, curve and turn the arms, palms facing inside, move towards the chest, follow by expanding outward, turn the palms forward, follow by deep, long and slow inhalation, expanding the chest cavity as much as possible (Figs. 2-1, 2-2).

Fig.2-2

Fig.2-3

2. Both arms parallel and approach each other in front of the chest, palms facing forward and then facing each other, turn the palms downward, lower the knees and squat, follow by deep and slow exhalation (Figs. 2-3, 2-4).

13

Fig.2-4

The above one raising and lowering, one inhalation and one exhalation is considered as one time, repeat 3 —5 times.

FUNCTIONS:

The chest cavity holds the heart and lung, lung controls the Qi, and heart the blood of the whole body. When the Qi moves the blood moves, when the Qi does not flow smoothly, the blood circulation is affected. There are two types of Qi: inborn and acquired, but both cannot dissociate from the oxygen of the blood.

This step has the good effects of increasing the breathing ability and the movement of Qi and blood, thus improving the functions of heart and lung through the opening and closing of the chest and the upward and downward diaphragm movements. Good for fear, short breathing, insomnia, dreaminess, forgetfulness, asthma, etc.

STEP 3: DANCING WITH THE RAINBOW

THEORY:

Dancing here means the two arms swinging up and down with one on the left and the other on the right. Rainbow is an optical phenomena in the sky. The tiny water drops in the sky gives rise to the coloured bands as the results of refraction of the sunlight. It has seven colours and is very beautiful, and makes one feel comfortable. This step means the two arms move as if you are holding the rainbow in the hands and swinging and dancing on the left and right. The external and internal concentrations are combined together, i.e. moving the concentration from the external rainbow to Laogong (P. 8) and filling it into the Baihui* (Du 20) with inhalation while moving up and exhalation while moving down. There are according to the general breathing principle.

METHOD:

---

*Baihui is located on the midpoint of the line connecting the apexes of the two auricles (Fig. 3).

Fig.3-1

Fig.3-2

1. From the last movement, when the knees are changing from the squatting to standing position, turn the palms from facing down to face each other, then raise up both arms in front of the chest and accompanying by inhalation (Figures. 3-1, 3-2).

16

Fig.3-3

2. Gradually move the head backwards, expand both arms to about shoulder height, palms facing up, accompanying by exhalation (Figure. 3-3).

Fig.3-4

3. Standing upright, supporting an imaginary ball on the head, gradually move body weight to the right foot, raise left sole, move left toes outwards 45 degrees, and meanwhile gradually raise right hand accompanying by inhalation. The left arm is still at shoulder height, palm facing upward (Figure. 3-4) and exhale when the right palm is facing the top of head (Baihui; Du. 20).

18

4. Gradually move the body weight towards left side, turn the left toes inwards 45 degrees back to original position, lower the left sole to ground, gradually raise the left arm upward and lower the right arm slowly to shoulder height, meanwhile lift up the right sole, turn left toes outwards 45 degrees accompanying by inhalation. While left palm is facing the top of the head the movement is accompanied by exhalation process.

The above one raising and lowering movement together with one inhalation and one exhalation is considered as one time, repeat 3—5 times for each of the left and the right sides.

FUNCTIONS:

The muscle groups at the back of shoulder and lumbar regions often suffer from sprain and pain due to improper postures. The gradual and gentle stretching and contraction of this step actively improve the blood circulation and lymph circulation of the muscles, remove the muscle fatigue and decrease the fat deposit. This step also has good effects in improving the joints of shoulder, elbow and wrist; it is a good step for the prevention and cure of sprains of lumbar and shoulder muscles, spinal problems and periarthritis of shoulder.

STEP 4: SEPARATING THE CLOUDS WITH SWINGING ARMS

THEORY:

This step means swinging both arms, separating the

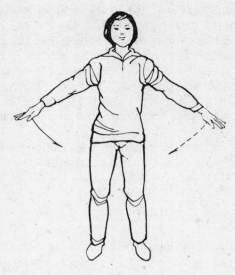

Fig.4-1

colourful clouds above the head; the movement is soft, gentle and forceful. This step uses the concentration on Laogong (P. 8) to blend with the external concentration. With the large movements of making the circles the blood and lymph circulations are fastened, particularly the blood and lymph circulation in the upper limbs. This results in promoting the pumping function of the heart, improving the function of the shoulder, knee and elbow joints.

This step still concentrates on Laogong (P. 8) to regulate the heart (mind), breathing and energy.

METHOD:

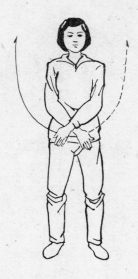

Fig.4- 2

1. From the previous movement, move back the right foot, body weight in between the two feet, gradually extend the left arm, both palms facing upwards at shoulder height; then turn the palms so that the center of the palms are gradually facing down, slowly lower both arms and cross in front of the body, normally the left hand is at the outer and the right hand is inner, meanwhile slowly lower the knees till they are on the same line with the toes, accompanying by exhalation (Figures. 4-1, 4-2).

Fig.4- 3

2. Gradually straighten both knees, lift up both arms and swing gradually in front of the chest and separate in front and above the head, palms facing outside and upward direction accompanying by inhalation (Figure. 4-3).

3. Gradually land both arms along both sides, palms slowly facing down and then facing back, meanwhile slowly lower both knees accompanying by exhalation movement (Figure. 4-2).

22

The above one raising and lowering movement together with one inhalation and one exhalation is considered as one time, repeat 3 - 5 times.

FUNCTIONS:

This is a good step in preventing arthritis around the shoulder joints because of the large circular movement of raising and lowering which has the effect of expanding the movement of the shoulder joints; it also improves the knee joints and breathing functions by the gradually lowering and straightening of the knees and the exercises of the thoracic muscles.

STEP 5: BACK ROLLING OF UPPER ARM IN FIXED STANCE

THEORY:

The external concentration is on the back rolling of upper arm while the internal concentration is at Laogong (P. 8) in the center of palms.

This step is derived from the "Back Swinging Monkey" step of Taiji Quan which is also known as "Back Rolling of the Humerus". Standing in the horse riding stance is normally called the "fixed stance" and "humerus" refers to the upper arm, "back rolling of upper arm" here describes the opposing movements of the two arms, one in front and one at the back.

This step emphasises on leading the Qi with concentration, moving the upper arm, shoulder joint and joints of the spine. It has the function of expanding the thorax and hence it is able to prevent and cure illness of the above joints and to regulate and improve breathing function.

The concentration of this step is at Laogong (P. 8), combining the external and internal concentrations to regulate the mind, breathing and energy.

METHOD:

1. From the previous movement, gradually stretch forward the left arm, palm facing up, stretch the right arm backward accompanying by inhalation. Next bend

Fig.5-1

Fig.5-2

the right arm upward, stretch fist forward passing by
the side of the ear, turn the palm down and squat in
horse riding stance (Figure. 5-1). Simultaneously bend
the left palm backward and the two palms face each
other in front of the left side of the chest, concentration
at the Laogong (P. 8) (Figure. 5-2) accompanying by

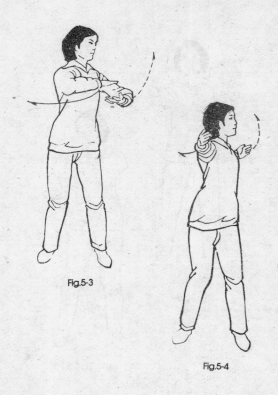

Fig.5-3

Fig.5-4

exhalation. After this, gradually turn the body leftward, rotate the right palm 180 degrees, turn the palms
(Figure. 5-3); extend the arms and expand the chest
and meanwhile straighten the knees. This movement is
accompanied by deep, slow, long and even inhalation
process (Figure. 5-4).

Fig.5-5

2. As above, do the rolling of upper arm on the other side, in the opposite direction (Figure. 5-5).

The above left and right movement is considered as one time, repeat 3—5 times.

FUNCTIONS:

This step involves larger movement of the upper arms and the thorax, the two Laogong (P. 8) acupoints are continuously close to each other thus strengthening internal regulatory functions and concentration. In addition the knees and the joints of the spine are also mildly exercised resulting in better physiological functions, breathing ability is improved and it is a good step for the prevention and cure of tracheitis and cold.

STEP 6: ROWING BOAT IN THE LAKE CENTER

THEORY:

The external concentration is "rowing boat in the lake center" while the internal concentration is at Laogong (P. 8) at the center of the palms.

The movement of this step is based on the picture of free and easy rowing of boat in the lake center. During the practice the internal concentration is still at Laogong (P. 8). This step regulates the mind, breathing and energy through the harmonious movements of all the joints of the body, especially the large joints of knee, ankle, hip, shoulder, elbow, and wrist and also the joints of spine, resulting in free flow of meridians, smooth joints and harmonious Qi and blood.

METHOD:

1. From the above movement, after rolling the upper arms, extending the arms and expanding the chest,

Fig.6-1

gradually turn the body back to center, let both arms
fall naturally inward, accompanying by exhalation
process during the movement (Figure. 6-1). Change

Fig.6-2

both hands into holding half fists, raise upward and place in front of the collar bones accompanying by inhalation (Figure. 6-2). Next lower the knees and

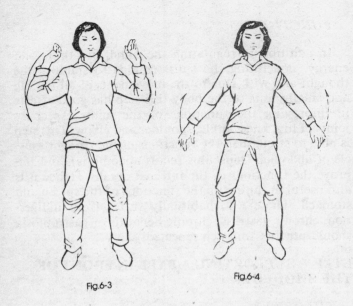

Fig.6-3

Fig.6-4

squat down, slowly extend the hands, with the palms facing front then facing down and facing back, make an arch-like movement of rowing boat accompanying by exhalation process (Figure. 6-3).

2. Gradually stretch both knees, slowly move and rotate the arms so that the palms are facing up and front, then place them in front of the collar bones with both hands half holding into fists (Figure. 6-4) accompanied by inhalation.

The above one raising and lowering movement is considered as one time, repeat 3—5 times.

FUNCTIONS:

In addition to regulating the mind, breathing and energy, nourishing the spirit (mind) to stabilise the thought and will. Due to the movements of all the big and small joints of the body this step has good effects in improving the functions of the joints especially joints of hip, knee, ankle, shoulder and elbow. This step is able to strengthen the functions of the straight muscle of abdomen (musculus rectus abdominis), and improve the functions of the internal organs. Hence it is also useful in tuning up the functions of the spleen and stomach. Those who habitually suffer from indigestion, chronic gastritis, chronic hepatitis or gastroptosia should practise this step repeatedly.

STEP 7: SUPPORTING A BALL IN FRONT OF THE SHOULDER

THEORY:

The movement is based on the picture of supporting a ball in front of the shoulder and this is the external concentration. The internal concentration is still in the Laogong (P. 8) at the palm centers. Practise left and right alternately and also alternate the concentration.

The left and right side alternating movement of this step can increase the extent of spine activities, improve the contraction and extension functions and the coordination of lumbar and back muscle groups. Similarly it can also increase the functions of the muscle groups around the shoulder joints and surrounding areas.

Fig.7-1

METHOD:

1. From the previous movement, gradually change the fists in front of the collar bones into palms, do not lower the knees any more, body stand relax and tranquil (Figure. 7-1), slowly move right hand and stretch towards the front of left shoulder, imagining you are supporting a ball and the internal concentration is at

Fig.7-2

Fig.7-3

Laogong (P. 8), palm facing upper left direction and meanwhile turn the body leftward 45 degrees, lift up the right sole, toes on ground and shift body weight to the left foot, accompanying by inhalation (Figure. 7-2). After this turn the right palm to face down, let it fall down slowly and naturally, lower the right sole, turn body back to original position accompanying by exhalation (Figure. 7-3).

Fig.7-4

2. In the same manner practise supporting a ball in front of the right shoulder, but in the opposite directions (Figures. 7-4).

The above left and right movement is considered as one time, repeat 3—5 times.

FUNCTIONS:

This step can get rid of the fatigue and strain of the lumbar and back muscle groups and increase their contraction and extension functions. It has definite good effects in the prevention and cure of shoulder periarthritis, problems of cervical and lumbar vertebrae, and in the improvement of breathing functions.

STEP 8: TURNING THE BODY TO GAZE AT THE MOON

THEORY:

The movement is based on the picture of turning the body and gazing at the moon. This is external concentration while the internal concentration of this step is still at Laogong (P. 8) of the palm centers. While raising the head, concentration on Laogong, picturing that you are gazing at the bright moon in the clear sky and combine both the external and internal concentrations to regulate the mind, breathing and energy.

This step covers bigger area of movement than the previous step of "supporting a ball in front of the shoulder", and improves the functions of the bones and the muscles of spine and shoulder joints.

METHOD:

1. From the previous movement, shift body weight slowly to the left foot, turn the body leftward 45 degrees, lift both arms high up in the upper-left direction, lift up right sole and lightly step on the right toes,

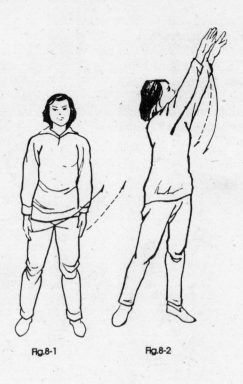

Fig.8-1   Fig.8-2

both palms facing front and then up, raise the head in the position of gazing at the moon but concentration is still at Laogong (P. 8), accompanying by inhalation process during the movement. After this, gradually lower both arms, turn body back to original position, lower the right sole to the ground and accompanied by exhalation (Figures. 8-1, 2).

2. Practise as above turning to the right and gaze at the moon (Figures. 8-3, 4).

The above left and right movement is considered as one time, repeat 3—5 times.

Fig.8-3

Fig.8-4

FUNCTIONS:

This step is basically similar to the previous step and has good effects for the various joints and muscles in the shoulder, neck and waist. It can also improve the breathing function and hence can prevent and treat periarthritis of the shoulder, hyperosteogeny of cervical and lumbar vertebrae, fatigue and injury of lumbar and back muscles, chronic tracheitis. Those who often suffer from the above problems should practise repeatedly.

STEP 9: TURNING WAIST AND PUSHING PALM

THEORY:

This step through the co-ordinated movements of "turning" and "pushing". Here "turning" may be taken as moving the Qi while "pushing" may be considered as generating energy and force. During the practice the concentration is at Laogong (P. 8). The concentration is internal only.

METHOD:

1. From the previous movement, bend both knees and attain the horse riding stance (see explanation in Step 10), slightly bend the elbows, change both hands to half fists and place them along the sides of waist, center of fists facing up (Figure. 9-1). Slowly turn the waist leftward 45 degrees, lift the right arm and accompanied by inhalation. Following this turn the wrist and

Fig.9-1   Fig.9-2

change fist into palm, push with internal force in
left-front direction, palm facing left-front direction
accompanying by exhalation (Figure. 9-2). After this
change palm into fist, fist facing up, bend the right arm
and bring back the right hand to the right side of the
waist (Figure. 9-3).

Fig.9-3

Fig.9-4

2. As above practise turning waist towards the right side and pushing the palm (Figure. 9-4).

The above left and right movement is considered as one time, repeat 3—5 times.

FUNCTIONS:

The "turning waist" movement strengthens the movement co-ordination of the muscle groups and joints of the waist and hip, hence this step has definite

41

usefulness in the prevention and cure of lumbar muscle strain, injury of piriformis and in improving the functions of lumbar vertebrae and reduce problems of lumbosacral joint. "Pushing palm" strengthens the movement co-ordination of cervical and thoraxic vertebrae, and shoulder and elbow joints. With long practice, the above functions and movements can be improved, it can also prevent and cure hyperosteogeny of the cervical vertebrae, shoulder periarthritis, strain and blood flow in the cerebral arteries.

STEP 10: HORSE RIDING STANCE WITH HANDS MOVING IN THE CLOUDS

THEORY:

External concentration is on the hands moving in the cloud while the internal concentration is at Laogong (P. 8).

"Horse riding stance" is a standing posture, it is like riding on a horse, i.e. both feet separated, both knees bending down, knee caps are not beyond the toes, coccyx in the middle, do not protrude the buttock backward, the upper body is straight, and body weight in the middle of both feet. "Moving hands in the clouds" is the state of moving the hand leftward and rightward like white clouds moving in the sky: light, carefree and natural. During the practice, let the internal concentration and external concentration meet, and with the spine as the axis, regulate the mind, breathing and energy by circulating the Qi in the left and right directions.

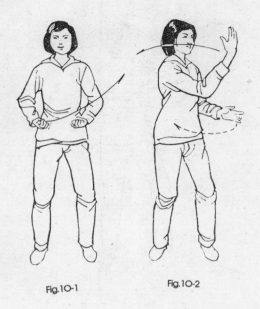

Fig.10-1   Fig.10-2

METHOD:

1. From the previous movement, after returning to the original body position, still in horse riding stance, hold both hands into half fists and place them at the sides of the waist (Figure. 10-1).

2. Gradually turn the upper body leftward 45 degrees, change both hands from fists to palms, right arm extend in left-front direction, slightly bend the elbow into an arch, palm facing the Yintang (extra) in be-

Fig. 10-3

tween the two eyebrows, left hand at the height of the nave with palm facing right, concentration at Lao-gong (P. 8) and accompanying by inhalation (Figure. 10-2). After this with the waist leading the movement* slowly turn the body from left to right accompanying by exhalation (Figure. 10-3).

---

*Waist leading: During the movements, it is always the waist that plays the leading role. For instance here, the waist move and this brings the body to move, not the other way round. With the waist leads the movement, the internal organs in the abdomen will perform some self-massage (From the translator).

Fig. 10-4

3. When turning to about 90 degrees to the right, slightly raise the body and left arm so that the palm center is at the height of Yintang (extra), lower the right arm slowly so that the right palm is at the height of the navel accompanying by inhalation, and with the same method turn the body from right to left (Figure. 10-4).

The above left and right movement is considered as one time, repeat 3—5 times.

Up to now, the first part of the exercises can have a time-out after doing the conclusion step. The second part of the exercises can be started after practising well the first part.

CONCLUSION STEP

METHOD:

1. Slightly bend the upper body, lower the knees and squat, slowly lower both arms to the sides of the knees accompanying by exhalation.

2. Slowly raise both hands imagining that they are carrying Qi, straighten the body and continue to carry both arms to the front of the forehead accompanying by deep, long and slow inhalation.

3. Turn the hands with palms facing down, slowly lower both arms along the front middle line, fill the body with Qi accompanying by deep, long and slow exhalation process. When the hands pass through the mouth, touch the upper palate with the tip of the tongue intentionally, then lower the tongue and continue the process of filling the Qi at Dantian.

4. Pile up the Laogong of both hands and place at the Dantian. For males, the left hand at the inside, while for females the right hand at the inside. Lift the kidney Qi 3—5 times (This is to lift up reproductive organ, contract the anus and meanwhile clinch the teeth).

5. Lift up the soles and then gradually relax and lower to the ground to conclude.

FUNCTIONS:

Regulate the mind, breathing and energy with the posture of the horse riding stance and moving hands in the clouds, with Yi (will) leading the Qi so that Qi reaches wherever Yi arrives and with the waist as axis lead the turning movement of the body. All these have definite usefulnesses in improving the functions of the nerves, in prevention and cure of lumbar muscles strain and injury, periarthritis of shoulder, hyperosteogeny and also in improving the internal organs.

THE SECOND PART:
from step 11 to 20

STEP 11: LEFT AND RIGHT DREDGING THE SEA AND LOOKING AT THE SKY

THEORY:

The external concentration is "dredging the sea and looking at the sky", the internal concentration is at Laogong (P. 8) in the middle of the palms.

This step describes the bending down of waist, stretching the arms and lifting the head and looking upwards at the sky as "dredging the sea and looking at the sky". "Sea" and "sky" give the impression of vastness and there are many ancient sayings about the sea and sky that encourage a person to be "open minded", throwing away worries during the practice and regulate the mind, breathing and energy with full heart and mind.

Taking into consideration the physiological functions of the left and right sides of the cerebrum, it is recommended to practise this step in the left and right sequences.

METHOD:

A. LEFT DREDGING THE SEA AND LOOKING AT THE SKY

1. From the previous movement, lean back slightly

Fig.11-1

the body, bend both arms backward, step out left foot in the left-front direction, the sole touching the ground first and accompanied by inhalation (Figure. 11-1). Next put the whole foot on the ground to form the left

Fig. 11-2

"bow stance"* and slowly bend the upper body forward, move the body weight forward, and cross both hands (from the sides) in front of the left knee, and accompanied by exhalation (Figure. 11-2).

---

*Bow stance is a posture in Chinese martial art, it is either on the left or right side. The left bow stance: Starting from standing feet parallel posture, step out left leg in the left-front direction, move body forward in the same direction, bend the left leg and keep the right leg slanting straight, body weight on the left leg. This is the posture for shooting arrows with the bow. Left toes point slightly to the right while right toes remain pointing forward. The reverse directions for right bow stance (From the translator).

Fig.11-3

2. Slowly lean the upper body backward, body weight shift to the back, gradually extend both arms, palm facing out and upward, lift the head like looking at the sky and accompanied by inhalation (Figure. 11-3). Following this bend the upper body forward, let the arms fall down naturally and again cross in front of the left knee accompanying by exhalation process during the movement (Figures. 11-1, 2).

The above sequence of inhalation and exhalation is considered as one time, repeat 3—5 times.

Fig.11-4

B. RIGHT DREDGING THE SEA AND LOOKING AT THE SKY

From the previous movement, slowly bend the upper body backward, shift body weight backward, and draw back the left leg while gradually extending both arms. After the left foot is firmly on ground, move the right leg half a step in the right-front direction, the sole on ground first and accompanied by inhalation. Next place the whole foot on ground, bend the upper body forward, cross both arms in front of the right knee and accompanying by exhalation (Figure. 11-4).

The above sequence of inhalation and exhalation is considered as one time, repeat 3—5 times.

FUNCTIONS:

This step involves bending the body forward and backward, deep inhalation and deep exhalation, it thus effectively strengthens the lumbar and back muscles and improves the movements of the knee, hip and shoulder joints. It also has the effects of providing an internal massage of heart, lung, liver, kidney, spleen, stomach and other internal organs resulting in overall co-ordination of the functions of all organs (viscera and bowels),* and smoothening the flow of Qi and blood in the meridians. The even, rhythmic and slow movements make one feels comfortable, easy and carefree during the practice.

This step has good co-ordinating and harmonising

---

*The terms organs, viscera and bowels have no standard English equivalents. Chinese medicine classifies the main internal parts of the body into five Zang and six Fu. The five Zang (organs or bowels) are the solid-organs and they are the Yin Orbs. These are the heart, the liver, the spleen, the lung and the kidney. On the other hand the six Fu (bowels) are the hollow-organs and they are the Yang Orbs. These are the gall bladder, the stomach, the small intestines, the large intestines, the urinary bladder and the Trijiao (Triple Burners or Triple Warmer). In addition to the five Zang a sixth one is sometimes included and this may be the pericardium or the Vital Gate (Gate of Life) according to different schools. It should be noted that in Chinese medicine the emphasis is laid on the various functions of an organ (viscera) or bowel rather than on its anatomical structure. The functions of an organ or bowel in the traditional Chinese medicine need not be the same as in the Western medicine (From the translator).

effects on various illnesses caused by malfunctioning of the internal organs. Some examples are malfunctioning of stomach and intestine, gastroptasia, chronic gastritis, chronic enteritis, malfunctioning of the vegetative nervous system, neurosism and also various slight pains of joints and muscle strains.

STEP 12: REGULATING QI IN UPWARD AND DOWNWARD MOVEMENTS

THEORY:

This is the calming down step after the previous step of "dredging the sea and looking at the sky". The calming effect is by regulating the mind, breathing and energy through slow inhalation during the upward movement and exhalation during the downward movement. The hand is used to assist the Yi (will), and using Yi to lead the Qi. This step is on internal concentration at he Laogong (P. 8).

METHOD:

1. From the previous movement, retract the right eg to the original position while slowly lean the upper body backward, shift the body weight backward, gradually lower the arms to both sides of the body and accompanied by exhalation.

Fig. 12-1   Fig. 12-2

2. With right palm facing down and concentration on Laogong (P. 8), lead the Qi to raise along the line in front of the left armpit, when the hand passes the shoulder change the palm to face out, and turn the palm to face up while passing through the head (Figures. 12-1, 2) accompanying by inhalation. Then slow-

Fig. 12-3

Fig. 12-4

ly guide the Qi to travel down to Dantian while passing through the face, chest and abdomen along the middle line accompanying by exhalation (Figure. 12-3).

3. As above regulate the Qi with the left hand (Figure. 12-4).

The above left and right movement is considered as one time, repeat 3—5 times.

FUNCTIONS:

Owing to the involvement of totally internal concentration in this step, one is especially easy to enter into the calm tranquil state and relax with natural breathing rhythm. It has good effects in regulating the physiological functions of the cerebral cortex, in strengthening the functions of internal organs, in curing neurosism, malfunctioning of the vegetative nerves of stomach and intestines, menopausal syndrome, hypertension and disorders due to internal injuries caused by the various emotions.*

---

*According to Chinese medicines, imbalance emotion is one of the causes of diseases. There are seven emotions, namely joy, anger, melancholy, anxiety, sorrow, fear and fright and these are considered as to be endogenous factors and the diseases caused are therefore "internal" as compared to diseases caused by external factors. The external factors refer to the six untimely weather influences, namely wind, cold, (summer) heat, dampness, dryness and fire (body heat due to untimely weather) (From the translator).

STEP 13: LEFT AND RIGHT PUSHING AND REINFORCING THE WAVES

THEORY:

The external concentration is "pushing and reinforcing the waves" while the internal concentration is at the Laogong (P. 8) in the middle of the palms.

This step simulates the picture of the up and down movements of the waves and billows in river and sea and uses the simulation to regulate the mind, breathing and energy. This is a method of Qigong practice combining internal and external concentrations with heaven, earth and man in correspondence. It involves up and down and raising and lowering movements which are not only beautiful but also relaxing and one feels comfortable after the practice.

METHOD:

A. LEFT PUSHING AND REINFORCING THE WAVES

1. From the previous movement, lower the right hand from the front middle line to the side of body, slowly bend both arms, slightly bend the fingers and place hands in front of the chest, palms change from facing down to facing front, at the same time shift body weight to the back and accompanied by inhalation. Next step left leg out in left-front direction, sole on ground first, shift body weight in front, with concentration push both arms along front-downward direction

Fig.13-1

Fig.13-2

accompanying by exhalation (Figure.13-1). Following this lift up the body, raise both arms in arches just like waves raising up, lift the sole of the back foot accompanying by inhalation (Figures. 13-2, 13-3).

Fig. 13-3

2. When the wave is at its crest, lower it with concentration, meanwhile shift the body weight backward, sole on ground, lift the toes of the front foot, lower both arms gradually to the lowest position of the wave and accompanied by exhalation. Next raise both the bending arms and return both hands to the upper front position of the chest accompanying by inhalation.

Repeat the above 3—5 times.

Fig.13-4

B. RIGHT PUSHING AND REINFORCING THE WAVES

1. From the previous movement, when the body weight is shifted backward and both arms (bending) are lifted up, retract the left leg, after placing it firmly, step out the right leg in right-front direction, sole on ground first accompanying by inhalation (Figure. 13-4).

2. Following this the whole foot is on the ground, shift body weight forward and practise the right pushing and reinforcing the waves movements.

Repeat the above 3—5 times.

FUNCTIONS:

This step ensures that all the parts of the body are moved, all the body joints are particularly able to be active during the practice and be co-ordinate. It increases the regulatory function of the cerebrum in the overall exercise and is good for neurosism. It improves the internal organs and bowels through the deep breathing during the upward and downward movement. During the practice, almost everyone feels very comfortable and likes to do a few more times. This particular step when practised alternately in both sides is better than only in one side.

STEP 14: SOOTHING THE CHEST AND ABDOMEN WITH QI

THEORY:

This step is the stabilising movement after the previous "pushing and reinforcing the waves" step. It soothes the chest and abdomen by moving the Qi through the concentration on Laogong (P. 8) resulting in regulating the mind, breathing and energy.

It regulates the functions and improves the vitality of all the meridians, internal organs and bowels and enhances their co-ordination.

It smoothens and tunes up all the meridians, internal organs and bowels and enhances their co-ordination. It therefore regulates their functions and improves their vitality.

Fig.14-1   Fig.14-2

METHOD:

1. From the previous movement, when the body weight is shifted backwards, bend and lift up both arms and simultaneously retract the right leg. After the leg is firmly placed, slowly lower both hands along the ribs to the sides of the hip accompanying by exhalation process.

2. Raise the right arm outward, high up from the side, accompanying by inhalation (Figure. 14-1). Next lower along the ear in the left downward direction, palm facing inward and soothe the chest and abdomen

Fig.14-3   Fig.14-4

with Qi. Point the fingers downwards in the chest, but move down the palm horizontally after passing through the diaphragm, accompanying by exhalation process during the movement, and lower the knees slightly (Figures. 14-1, 2) during the exhalation.

3. Raise the left arm and soothe the chest and abdomen with the Qi in the right side, following the above procedures (Figures. 14-3, 4).

The above left and right movement is considered as one time, repeat 3—5 times.

FUNCTIONS:

This step is totally led by internal concentration. It is able to expand the chest, improve the diaphragm, regulate the stomach and intestine, soothe the liver and improve the gall bladder, nourish the kidney and pacify the heart. It is therefore effective for patients who suffer from imbalance of internal organs and emotions. Meanwhile it is also able to smoothen the joints of shoulder and elbow. Hence it is recommended for those who suffer from the following illnesses to practise this step more often: sensation of fullness in the chest and diaphragm, chronic indigestion, disorders of the gastro-intestinal tract, improper functioning of heart and lung, malfunctioning of nerves system, forgetfulness and insomnia.

STEP 15: LEFT AND RIGHT FLYING PIGEON SPREADING THE WINGS

THEORY:

The external concentration is "flying pigeon spreading the wings" while the internal concentration is at Laogong (P. 8) in the middle of the palms.

In this step the internal concentration is initiated through the beautiful carefree movements of the flying pigeon spreading its gliding wings. With the internal concentration it regulates the mind, breathing and energy. On combining the external concentration with the internal concentration and harmonising the correspondence of heaven, earth and man, i. reinforces the intimate relationship between body and the environment.

METHOD:

A. LEFT FLYING PIGEON SPREADING THE WINGS

1. From the previous movement gradually shift the body weight to the right leg, extend the arms outward, palm facing front and meanwhile bring the left leg half a step in the left-front direction (Figure. 15-1) accom-

Fig.15-1

Fig.15-2

Fig.15-3

panying by inhalation. Next move body weight forward, slowly bring the arms forward together, palms facing each other at shoulder width, accompanying by exhalation in left bow stance (Figure. 15-2).

2. Gradually shift the body weight backward, bend both arms, retract the palms inward (Figure. 15-3), then slowly spread out accompanying by inhalation.

Repeat the above 3—5 times.

Fig. 15-4

B. RIGHT FLYING PIGEON SPREADING THE WINGS

1. From the previous movement retract the left leg while shifting the body weight slowly backward, continue to spread both arms and accompanying by inhalation.

2. Practise the right flying pigeon spreading wings as above (Figure. 15-4).

Repeat the above 3—5 times.

FUNCTIONS:

Due to the shifting of body weight backward and forward together with the spreading and closing of the both arms, this step effectively expands the thorax, increases the lung breathing capacity and moves all the joints. It has the effect of calming the heart, pacifying the soul, easing the chest and smoothening the breathing. It is recommended that those who suffer from the following diseases practise repeatedly to obtain results: chronic problems of the respiratory systems such as bronchitis, emphysema of lungs, and also problems of the nervous and the circulatory systems such as neurosism, insufficient blood supply to cerebrum, cerebral arteriosclerosis, insufficient blood supply to coronary artery, and also problems related to the functions of the digestive system.

STEP 16: DOUBLE DRAGONS SPIRALLING ON THE PILLAR

THEORY:

The external concentration is "double dragons spiralling on the pillar" while the internal concentration is sinking the Qi at Dantian.

This step imitates two dragons spiralling on the pillar, alternately raising up and lowering down and this leads the internal concentration to regulate the mind, breathing and energy resulting in co-ordinated movements of all the joints in the body.

Fig. 16-1

METHOD:

1. From the previous movement retract the right leg to original position while expanding the arms and shifting back the body weight. This is accompanied by inhalation. Next change the palms to face downward and lower them naturally to the sides of the body accompanying by exhalation.

2. With the waist as axis, lead the right arm to move toward the front of left shoulder, left arm towards the back of the right hip, swing them in forward and backward meanwhile change palms into half fists accompanying by inhalation (Figure. 16-1).

Fig.16-2

3. Lower the knees to squat in the horse riding stance, upper body in upright position, coccyx right in the middle, imagine supporting a light object on the head, accompanying by exhalation (Figure. 16-2).

Fig.16-3   Fig.16-4

4. Straighten both knees, change both fists into palms and practise as above. The left arm swings toward the front of right shoulder, the right arm swings towards the back of left hip, and at the same time change palms to half fists, accompanying by inhalation. Lower the knees, squat and accompanied by exhalation in the horse riding stance (Figures. 16-3, 4).

The above left and right movement is considered as one time, repeat 3—5 times.

FUNCTIONS:

This step effectively strengthens the movement and function of the shoulder, knee and hip joints. It also enables the Qi of Dantian to circulate up and down in the body together with concentration (Yi Nian). It has good effects in improving the regulatory function of the cerebral cortex and in the prevention and cure of diseases of knee, shoulder and hip joints.

STEP 17: LEFT AND RIGHT GRASPING THE TAIL OF SPARROW

THEORY:

The external concentration is "grasping the tail of sparrow", alternating between stretching and bending and also between tension and relaxation, the internal concentration is at Laogong (P. 8) during the four sequences of Peng (making a shed), Luo (rubbing along), Ji (squeezing) and An (pressing). The mind, breathing and energy are regulated through the "left and right grasping the tail of sparrow". This is a very important step in the Taiji Quan. It is important to remember that during the practice one uses the will (Yi) and not the force, i.e. the internal concentration must be strong. This means that do not use brutal force but use the internal force, i.e. using the internal concentration to lead the Qi so that the will (Yi), Qi and energy all occur together.

Fig.17-1

METHOD:

A. LEFT GRASPING THE TAIL OF SPARROW

1. Left Carrying a Ball: From the previous movement, first turn the body slightly rightward, meanwhile row the right hand backward in an arch and raise up horizontally as the body turns, the centers of both hands facing each other in front of the right rib. The posture is like carrying and holding a ball, the body weight is at the right leg, hang the left foot in the inner side of the right foot with left toes touching the ground and accompanied by inhalation (Figure. 17-1).

Fig.17-2

2. Left Peng (making a shed): Turn the upper body slightly to the right, step out the left leg in the left-front direction in left bow stance, meanwhile move up the left arm toward the left-front direction accompanying by exhalation. The requirements are that the left arm is bent to form a horizontal bow and push, with the outer side of the lower arm and also the back of hand, in the forward direction. The left arm is at shoulder height, the left palm facing backward, the right hand lowers to the side of right hip along the right down direction, hand facing down, fingers pointing front, eyes at the left lower arm and concentrates at Laogong (Figure. 17-2).

Fig. 17-3   Fig. 17-4

3. Left Luo (rubbing along): Turn the body slightly to the left followed by stretching the left hand forward, and turning the palm to face downward, turn the right palm to face upward, move forward till it is below the left arm. Next bring down both hands accompanied by inhalation. This step involves turning the upper body rightward, both hands passing the abdomen and arch up along the right and backward direction until the right palm is facing upward at shoulder height (Figure. 17-3), bend left arm at horizontal level, palm facing backward, meanwhile shift the body weight to the right leg (Figure. 17-4).

Fig. 17-5

4. Left Ji (squeezing): Turn body slightly toward left, bend right elbow and fold back right arm, right hand gets close to the inner side of left wrist at a distance of about 5 cm, continue to turn the upper body leftward and slowly squeeze both hands forward, left palm facing back while right palm facing front, left lower arm should be kept semi-circular and meanwhile shift the body weight forward slowly to attain the posture of left bow stance (Figure. 17-5) accompanying by exhalation.

Fig. 17-6

5. Left An (pressing): Turn the left hand so that left palm is facing downward, move the right hand forward above the wrist, toward the right, then stretch forward at the same height as the left hand, palm facing down. Separate the two hands in left and right directions to shoulder width and accompanied by inhalation. Next bend the right knee, the upper body slowly sits back, shift body weight to the right leg, lift up left toes, meanwhile bend both elbows and draw back both hands to the front of waist, both hands pushing along front down direction (Figure. 17-6).

Fig.17-7

6. Left Tui (pushing): Shift the body weight slowly forward and at the same time push both centers of the palms forward and upward to attain the left bow stance again, accompanying by exhalation, with eyes looking horizontally and concentration is still at Laogong (P 8) (Figure. 17-7).

Fig. 17-8

B. RIGHT GRASPING THE TAIL OF SPARROW

Following the above movement, the upper body sits back slowly, meanwhile both arms turn rightward (Figure. 17-8), retract the left leg to shoulder width once the body weight is shifted to the right leg, following this, turn the body leftward and shift the body weight to the left leg again, meanwhile place the right hand in front of the left rib by drawing an arch, palm facing up. Bend left arm horizontally in front of the chest, both palms facing each other in the posture of "right

Fig. 17-9

carrying a ball" (Figure. 17-9), meanwhile retract the right leg and hang the right foot in the inner side of the left foot, right toes touching the ground. Step out right leg in the right-front direction to form right bow stance, and proceed to practise the right Peng, right Luo, right Ji, right An and right Tui sequences, except that the left and right directions are reversed.

Finally, sit back the upper body and turn leftward, simultaneously turn both arms leftward, slowly shift the body weight to the left leg and retract the right leg at shoulder width. Lower both arms naturally while the body weight settles at the middle between both legs.

Normally the above is practised once, but it may be repeated 3—5 times.

FUNCTIONS:

This is the core step of Taiji Quan and it reappears in many occasions. It has both the concentration of the pugilism and the energy of the forceful movement of martial arts (Gongfu), with the hand supporting the Yi (will and concentration) and the Yi leading the Qi. The movements are both heavy and light, forceful and yet gentle, with tranquillity while in motion, non-step and with step by step continuity, gentle, smooth and lively. By practising this step often, the internal concentration, will and spirit can be expressed, and it is able to combine the "concentration (Yi), vital force (Qi) and spirit (Shen)" and hence it has good effects in regulating the physiology and function of the central nervous system. It also can prevent and cure neurosism, insomnia, dreaminess, menopausal syndrome and brain fag. In addition, the turning of hip and waist and the stretching and bending of joints help to improve the physiology and function of the joints and is good for prevention and cure of joint problems.

STEP 18: CARRYING AND FILLING WITH QI

THEORY:

The external concentration is the entire nature, the internal concentration is to fill the Qi in the Dantian. The movements involve a series of lowering the knees and squatting, standing up and raising the arms and filling the Qi into Dantian. This enables one to regulate the mind, breathing and energy producing in the continuous and never ending harmonious correspondence of heaven, earth and man. The functions of all the body joints and muscles are therefore improved.

METHOD:

1. From the previous movement, stretch both arms outward slowly and lift them upward accompanying by inhalation (Figure. 18-1).

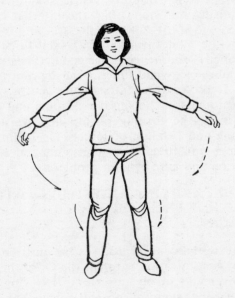

Fig.18-1

Fig. 18-2

2. Slightly bend the upper body, lower the knees and squat, slowly lower both arms to the sides of the knees (Figure. 18-2) accompanying by exhalation.

Fig. 18-3

3. Slowly raise both hands imagining that they are càrrying Qi, straighten the body and continue to carry both arms to the front of forehead accompanying by deep, long and slow inhalation (Figure. 18-3).

Fig. 18-4

4. Turn the hands with palms facing down, slowly lower both arms along the front middle line, fill the body with the Qi accompanying by deep, long and slow exhalation process. When the hands pass through the mouth, touch the upper palate with the tip of the tongue intentionally, then lower the tongue and continue the process of filling the Qi at Dantian (Figure. 18-4).

The above one raising and lowering movement together with one inhalation and one exhalation is considered as one time, repeat 3—5 times.

87

FUNCTIONS:

This step involves larger extent of exchanging internal and external Qi, it thus improves the lung capacity and the function of the lungs, resulting in higher oxygen content in the blood and it has the important function of improving the metabolism. It has definite curative values for chronic bronchitis, tuberculosis of lungs and other types of chronic problems.

STEP 19: CLOSED PALMS IN HORSE RIDING STANCE

THEORY:

This step regulates the mind, breathing and energy by combining the internal concentration at the Laogong (P 8) of both palms. The movements of this step are slow and gentle and they can guide and lead the Qi to sink down to Dantian. This step mainly strengthens the regulatory functions of the body and leads the cerebrum to tranquillity.

Fig. 19-1

METHOD:

1. From the previous movement extend both arms outward in 45 degrees, palms facing back, lower both knees and squat into horse riding stance accompanying by inhalation process during the movement (Figure. 19-1). Next turn the palms to face inward and upward,

Fig. 19-2

Fig. 19-3

send the Qi in the inward and downward direction along the groin, upper body remains upright, coccyx in the middle accompanying by exhalation process (Figure. 19-2).

2. Slowly stretch both knees, lift up both arms gradually, palms facing in, fingers pointing up and accompanied by inhalation (Figure. 19-3).

Fig.19-3   Fig.19-4

3. Close palms in front of the forehead, slowly lower along the front middle line (Ren meridian) accompanying by exhalation (Figure. 19-4). Separate both palms when the Qi is sent to Dantian, and again extend both arms outward 45 degrees and repeat as above.

The above one raising and lowering movement together with one inhalation and one exhalation is considered as one time, repeat 3—5 times.

FUNCTIONS:

On combining both palms with concentration (Yi) and guiding the Qi with will power (Nian) to sink the Qi at Dantian, this step is able to pacify the heart and to relax the body and it has good effects in relaxing and regulating the physiology and functions of cerebrum. It has definite curative purpose for those who suffer from neurosism, insomnia, dreaminess, irritability and agitation, excessive mental work and over anxiety. It can increase the lung capacity and the blood oxygen content for those who suffer from chronic bronchitis.

STEP 20: STRETCHING THE ARM WHILE CHARGING THE FIST

THEORY:

The external concentration is charging the fist forward with force while stretching the arm, the internal concentration is at Laogong (P. 8) in the middle of the palms. Moving the Qi from Dantian regulates the mind, breathing and energy, through the stretching of arm with forceful charging fist. This is a martial art step to strengthen the body. During the practice emphasis is on the concentration and not on the force, i.e. the internal concentration should be strong.

Fig.20-1   Fig.20-2

METHOD:

1. From the previous movement, both hands holding in half fists, the center of the fists facing up, place the fists at the sides of the body in horse riding stance (Figure. 20-1). Slowly lift up the right arm, change the fist to face down and accompanied by inhalation process. Next further push the center of the right fist forward and accompanied by exhalation (Figure. 20-2).

Fig.20-3

Fig.20-4

2. Turn the right fist to face up, retract right arm to original position and meanwhile gradually lift up the left arm, turn left fist to face down and accompanying by inhalation.

3. Turn the center of left fist to face front and push it forward accompanying by exhalation (Figure. 20-3). Next turn the center of fist to face up, retract left arm to original position (Figure. 20-4).

The above left and right movement is considered as one time, repeat 3—5 times.

Up to now, the second part of the exercises can have a time-out after doing the conclusion step. The third part of the exercises can be started after practising well the second part. The conclusion step is the same one mentioned in the first part.

FUNCTIONS:

This step demonstrates the internal force of the charging fist. The "internal force" is also known as internal Gongfu and in here it means supporting the Yi (will) with the hand, leading the Qi with Yi so that the Qi arrives where ever the Yi reaches and the strength and power (Li) reaches where ever the Qi goes. The concentration of this step originates from Dantian, travels upward to Shanzhong (Ren. 17), then passes through shoulder, elbow and wrist to generate the force through Laogong (P. 8). This results in the feeling of strong continuing force from the Qi during the practice. This has good effect in strengthening the functions of meridians, tendons, organs and viscera. It is a preferred step in the prevention and cure of general weakness, neurosism, short of breath and palpitation due to retarded function of the lungs.

THE THIRD PART:
from step 21 to 28

STEP 21: THE FLYING BIG WILD GOOSE

THEORY:

The external concentration is a big wild goose flying in the wide open sky, the internal concentration rises and lowers at Laogong (P. 8) in the middle of the palms. This step imitates the picture of a big wild goose flying freely in the wide open sky to regulate the mind, breathing and energy. The flight of the big wild goose is not only beautiful, it also enables one to feel comfortable and free. Furthermore since the internal concentration is at Laogong (P. 8) in the middle of the palms, it stimulates the Qi and blood circulation in the body when the internal concentration combines with the external concentration.

Fig.21-1

METHOD:

1. From the previous movement, change the horse riding stance to relax and tranquil standing posture, change fists to palms, lower both arms naturally at the sides accompanying by exhalation (Figure. 21-1).

Fig.21-2

2. Gradually raise high both arms from the sides, bend elbows and wrists, turn palms to face out and up, meanwhile raise the upper body, lift up the soles accompanying by inhalation (Figure. 21-2).

Fig.21-3

3. Lower both arms gradually and naturally, the wrist joints should be particularly soft, the center of palms should have feeling of Qi, meanwhile lower both soles to the ground, slowly lower the knees and squat to the horse riding stance accompanying by exhalation (Figure. 21-3).

The above raising up and lowering down sequence is considered as one time, repeat 3—5 times.

FUNCTIONS:

The movements of this step are natural, smooth and gentle, they enable one to relax and to fell comfortable, carefree and joyous after the practice. The up and down, and the lowering and raising movements strengthen the breathing function and gaseous exchange of the lungs. The co-ordinated movements smoothen all the joints of the body. The step can prevent and cure various problems such as chronic diseases due to unhappiness and blockage of Qi and blood, bronchitis and pains of joints.

STEP 22: THE ROTATING FLYWHEEL

THEORY:

The external concentration is the "rotating flywheel" moving forward continuously, the internal concentration is at Laogong (P. 8) in the middle of the palms. This step simulates the spine into a rotating flywheel to regulate the mind, breathing and energy. This rather large extent of rotation will surely increase and strengthen the functions of the various joints in the hip, shoulder and back, improve the exercises of the lumbar and back muscle groups and also has the effect of massaging the internal organs.

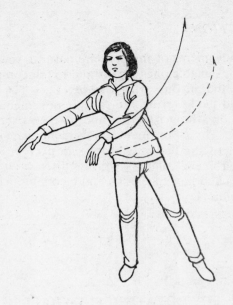

Fig.22-1

METHOD:

1. From the above movement move the left leg leftward half a step, meanwhile move both arms initially slightly toward the right then followed by moving leftward and upward, turn the waist in rotating movement (Figure. 22-1) accompanying by inhalation.

102

Fig.22-2

When the hands are lowering from above the head to lower-right side the movement is accompanied by exhalation (Figure. 22-2).

Fig.22-3

2. With the same method rotate the flywheel from left to right (Figures. 22-3, 4).

Fig.22-4

The above left and right movement is considered as one time, repeat 3—5 times.

FUNCTIONS:

This step involves rather large movements of the body and limbs and strong actions, hence one feels stretching of the waist, back and four limbs during the practice. This step is good for the recovery from diseases of cervical and lumbar vertebrae and also from problems of shoulder and hip joints. It is able to lighten the injury and strain of lumbar and back muscle groups by balancing the lumbar and back muscles. The rotating movements and exercises also strengthen the blood and lymph circulations and improve the functions of the vegetative autonomic nerves.

STEP 23: THE THREE YIN MERIDIANS OF THE LEFT AND RIGHT ARMS (TRAVELLING FROM CHEST TO HANDS)

Reference: Shisi Jingxue Tujie (Illustrated Acupoints of the Fourteen Meridians); Jianmei Jinluo Tu (Meridian Charts for Health and Beauty).

THEORY:

This step calls for internal concentration only, i.e. with the hand assisting the will (Yi), the Yi leading the Qi, guiding along the meridians to regulate the mind, breathing and energy.

The "three Yin of the arm" refers to the three Yin meridians. These are the Lung Meridian, the Heart Meridian and the Pericardium Meridian. These three meridians all travel from the chest to the hands. The first Yin is the Taiyin Lung Meridian of the Arm, it originates from the lung, travels under the collar bone of the chest and arrives at the tip of the thumb; the second Yin is the Shaoyin Heart Meridian of the Arm, it originates from the heart, travels under the armpit and arrives at the inner side of the small finger; the third Yin is the Jueyin Pericardium Meridian of the Arm, it originates from the pericardium, travels along the outer side of the breast and arrives at the tip of the middle finger. The lungs take charge of the Qi of the whole body, the heart takes charge of the blood, the heart and the pericardium together take charge of the spirit and mind. Hence on practising the Qigong along the meridians one can smoothen the flow of the meridians, regulate the Qi and blood and also strengthen the functions of the heart and lungs.

If one can remember some important acupoints during the practice the effects are so much better, the thinking and memory abilities can be increased.

The first Yin is the Lung Meridian of the Hand-Taiyin, the first point of this meridian is Zhongfu (L. 1); Shaoshang (L. 11) is the terminal point.

The second Yin is the Heart Meridian of the Hand-Shaoyin, the first point of this meridian is Jiquan (H. 1); Shaochong (H. 9) is the terminal point.

The third Yin is the Pericardium Meridian of the Hand-Jueyin, the first point of this meridian is Tainchi (P. 1); Zhongchong (P. 9) is the terminal point.

1 Zhongfu (L. 1): Below the acromial extremity of the clavicle, in the 2nd intercostal space, 6 *cun* to the side of the Ren Meridian.

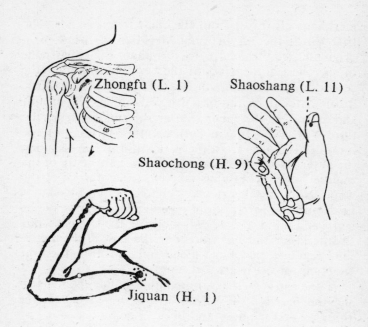

Zhongfu (L. 1)

Shaoshang (L. 11)

Shaochong (H. 9)

Jiquan (H. 1)

2 Shaoshang (L. 11): On the radial side of the thumb, about 0.1 *cun* behind the corner of the nail.

3 Jiquan (H. 1): In the center the axilla, on the medial side of axillary artery.

4 Shaochong (H. 9): On the radial side of the little finger, about 0.1 *cun* behind the corner of the nail.

5 Tainchi: (P. 1): One *cun* lateral to the nipple, in the fourth intercostal space.

6 Zhongchong (P. 9): In the center of the tip of the middle finger.

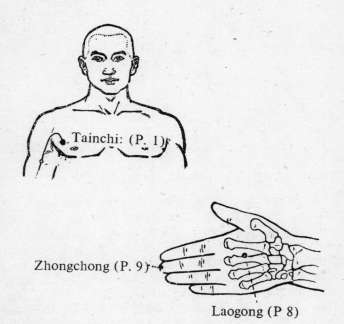

Tainchi: (P. 1)

Zhongchong (P. 9)

Laogong (P 8)

METHOD:

A. THE THREE YIN MERIDIANS OF THE LEFT ARM

Fig.23-1

1. From the last movement, when both arms are moving along the backward and upward direction, shift the body weight to the right leg, slowly turn the body rightward 45 degrees, retract the left foot and hang in the inner side of the right foot with toes touching the ground. Bend the left arm horizontally, sink the shoulder, fall the elbow, relax the wrist and turn in slightly. Bend the right arm, right hand in "sword fingers" posture*, fingers pointing below the left collar bone (Figure. 23-1) accompanying by inhalation.

2. Firstly moving the Qi along the left lung meridian: Move left leg one step leftward, left toes pointing

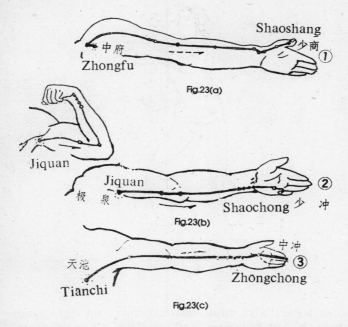

Shaoshang
中府 少商 ①
Zhongfu

Fig.23(a)

Jiquan

极泉 Jiquan
Shaochong 少冲 ②

Fig.23(b)

天池 中冲 ③
Tianchi Zhōngchōng

Fig.23(c)

in the front and outer direction. Slowly turn the body from right to left, with the waist leading**, move the

---

*Sword fingers: This is a posture in the Chinese martial art during the sword play. Normally the sword is held by the right hand, and the left hand is in the "sword finger" posture. Here both the second and third fingers are pointing out together, the thumb is placed on top of the fourth finger; the thumb, fourth and fifth fingers are bending inward on the palm to form a semi-fist. Similarly for the right sword finger posture.

**Waist leading the movement emphasises that the waist moves and makes the shoulder and arm to move along, not the other way round. Please also see the Note of Step 10. (from the Translator)

Fig.23-2

shoulder and arm, simultaneously move the right hand along the left lung meridian travelling along the front of the inner side of the upper limb and move the Qi to the tip of the left thumb, posture in left bow stance (Figure. 23-2) accompanying by exhalation. Next shift the body weight backward, the body sits backward and gradually turn rightward. At this moment, right hand leaves the left thumb, bend left arm horizontally again, sink the shoulder, fall the elbow and relax the wrist. Turn the lower arm inward, the small finger of the right hand pointing up under the left armpit with the other fingers bending accompanying by inhalation.

112

Fig.23-3

3. Secondly moving the Qi along the Heart Meridian: As the above procedure, move the Qi to the tip of the left small finger following the left Heart Meridian along the back of the inner side of the upper limb accompanying by exhalation (Figure. 23-3).

4. Thirdly moving the Qi along the left Pericardium Meridian: As the above procedure, with the pointing middle finger following the left Pericardium Meridian along the middle of the inner side of the upper limb, move the Qi to the left middle finger accompanying by exhalation.

Fig.23-4

B. THE THREE YIN MERIDIANS OF THE RIGHT ARM

1. Rotate the Hand and Exchange: From the last movement, retract the right leg and keep the foot close to the left foot, next turn the upper body leftward 45 degrees again, end right arm horizontally in the left-front direction, sink the shoulder, fall the elbow, relax the wrist. Turn the right arm slightly inward, bend left arm, left thumb pointing below the right collar bone (Figure. 23-4).

Fig.23-5

2. Retract right leg and move one step rightward, practise the three Yin meridians of the right arm as above, i.e. firstly moving the Qi along the right Lung Meridian, next along the right Heart Meridian and thirdly along the right Pericardium Meridian (Figure. 23-5).

FUNCTIONS:

The main purpose of this step is to improve the physiological functions of the three meridians of the lung, the heart and the pericardium. The lungs take charge of the Qi of the whole body, the heart takes charge of the blood, the heart and the pericardium together take charge of the spirit and mind. Hence on practising the Qigong along the meridians and regulating the heart (mind) and breathing, one can ensure smooth flow of the meridians and regulated Qi and blood. This can prevent and cure problems of the respiratory, heart and circulatory and also the nervous systems. It can also help one to relieve stuffiness of the chest and regulate the Qi, improve the Qi and nourish the Yin.

STEP 24: THE THREE YANG MERIDIANS OF THE LEFT AND RIGHT ARMS (TRAVELLING FROM HANDS TO HEAD)

Reference as in Step 23.

THEORY:

The "Three Yang of the Arm" means that in a addition to the three Yin Meridians, there are also three Yang Meridians, namely: the Large Intestine, the Small Intestine and the Trijiao (the Triple Warmer) Meridians in the arm. They all travel from the hands to Dazhui (Du 14) and then to the head. The first Yang is the Yangming Large Intestine Meridian of the Arm, from the tip of the second finger to Dazhui (Du 14) and goes up to the sides of the nose. The second Yang is the Taiyang Small Intestine Meridian of the Arm, travelling from the tip of the small finger and up to the ear and eye through Dazhui (Du 14). The third Yang is the Shaoyang Triple Warmer Meridian of the Arm, travelling from the tip of the fourth finger up to the ear and eye through Dazhui (Du 14). Dazhui (Du 14) is an acupoint at the back below the highest bone (the seventh cervical vertebra). The large and small intestines are important organs for the digestion, assimilation and excretion and for the maintenance of the normal body metabolism, the Triple Warmer are the important tracts for the Qi, blood and the body fluids. The practice of this step can help to smoothen the flow of the meridians, regulate and harmonise the Qi and blood, and improve the digestive functions.

This step calls for internal concentration only, i.e. with the hand assisting the will (Yi), the Yi leading the Qi, the Qi arrives wherever the Yi reaches, to regulate the mind, breathing and energy. If one can remember some important acupoints during the practice the effects are so much better, the thinking and memory abilities can be increased.

The first Yang is the large Intestine Meridian of Hand-Yangming, the first point of this meridian is Shangyang (LI. 1); Yingxiang (LI. 20) is the terminal point.

The second Yang is the Small Intestine Meridian of Hand-Taiyang, the first point of this meridian is Shaoze (SI. 1); Tinggong (SI. 19) is the terminal point.

The third Yang is the Sanjiao Meridian of the Hand-Shaoyang, the first point of this meridian is Guanchong (SJ. 1); Sizhukong (SJ. 23) is the terminal point.

1 Shangyang (LI. 1): On the radial side of the index finger, about 0.1 *cun* behind the corner of the nail.

2 Yingxiang (LI. 20): In the naso-labial groove, at the center of the outer side of the nostrils.

3 Shaoze (SI. 1): On the ulnar side of the little finger, about 0.1 *cun* behind the corner of the nail.

4 Tinggong (SI. 19): Between the tragus and the mandibuler joint, where a depression is formed when the mouth is slightly open.

5 Guanchong (SJ. 1): On the side of the ring finger, about 0.1 *cun* behind the corner of the nail.

6 Sizhukong (SJ. 23): In the depression at the lateral end of the eyebrow.

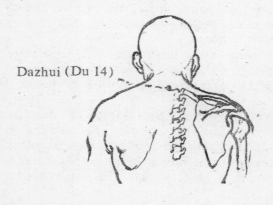

Dazhui (Du 14)

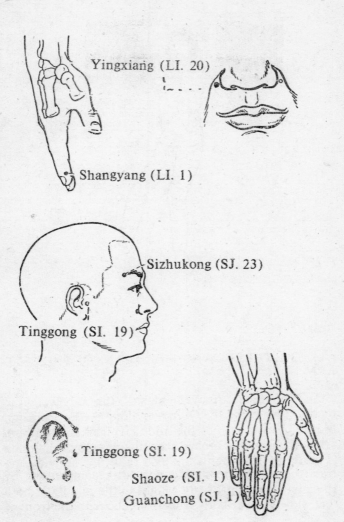

Yingxiang (LI. 20)

Shangyang (LI. 1)

Sizhukong (SJ. 23)

Tinggong (SI. 19)

Tinggong (SI. 19)

Shaoze (SI. 1)

Guanchong (SJ. 1)

Fig. 24-1

METHOD:

A. THE THREE YANG MERIDIANS OF THE LEFT ARM

1. From the last movement, shift the body weight to the right leg while the Qi moves along the Pericardium Meridian to the tip of the middle finger. Lift up both arms like drawing arches accompanying by inhalation (Figure. 24-1). Meanwhile also raise up the body, retract the left leg to shoulder width accompanying by the inhalation, shift body weight to the middle of both feet, slowly lower both arms from above to the front of

Fig.24-2

chest, turn palms to face inside and downward accompanying by exhalation. The concentration is at the finger tips (Figure. 24-2).

Gradually shift the body weight to the left leg, bend the left knee, turn right foot outward 90 degrees followed by turning slowly the body rightward 90 degrees, shift body weight forward, stretch both arms forward, lift up the left leg and move backward a small half step, right second finger pointing the left second finger and posture in right bow stance accompanying by exhalation (Figure. 24-3).

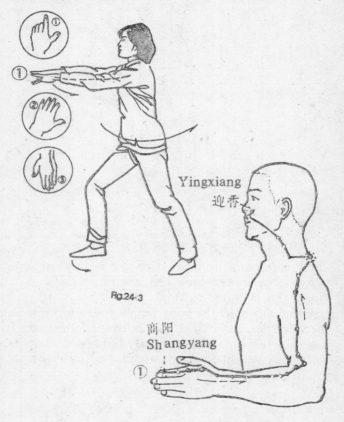

Fig.24-3

Yingxiang
迎香

商阳
Shangyang

Fig.24-4

2. Firstly moving the Qi along the Left Large Intestine Meridian: Shift body weight backward, lift up the right toes, with sole as axis, on one side turn leftward (with the waist leading the move) for about 135 degrees and on the other side the right "sword finger" pointing along the Large Intestine Meridian move the Qi to Dazhui (Du 14), but the concentration reaches the side of the nose accompanying by inhalation (Figures. 24-3, 4).

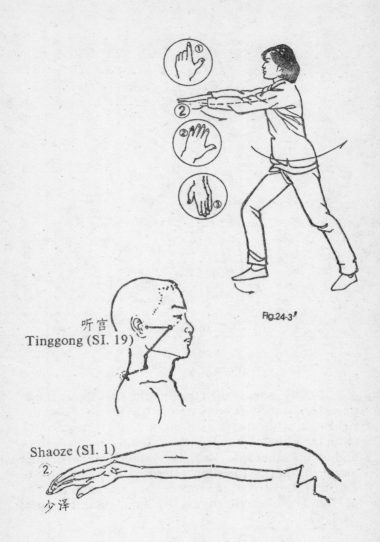

Fig.24-3'

听宫
Tinggong (SI. 19)

Shaoze (SI. 1)
②
少泽

124

3. Secondly moving the Qi along the Left Small Intestine Meridian: Lift up the left toes, turn body back to original position, posture in right bow stance, body weight on the right foot, point the second finger at the tip of the small finger accompanying by exhalation process, move the Qi to Dazhui (Du 14) as the above method but the concentration reaches the ear and eye, accompanying by inhalation (Figures. 24-3 (2), 24-4).

Fig.24-4'

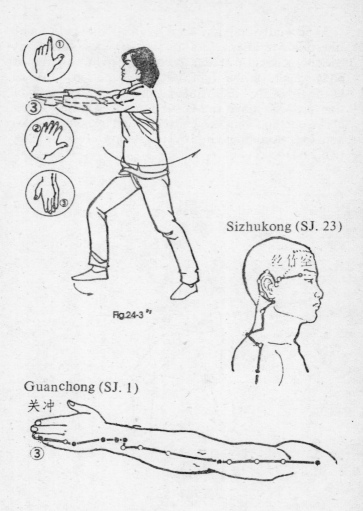

Fig. 24-3

Sizhukong (SJ. 23)

丝竹空

Guanchong (SJ. 1)
关冲
③

126

Fig.24-4

4. Thirdly moving the Qi along the Left Triple Warmer Meridian: As above turn body rightward accompanying by exhalation, posture in right bow stance, with the second finger pointing at the tip of the fourth finger. Move the Qi along the Triple Warmer Meridian to Dazhui (Du 14) but the concentration reaches ear and eye, accompanying by inhalation process (Figure. 24-3 (3), 24-4).

B. THE THREE YANG MERIDIANS OF THE RIGHT ARM

1. From the last movement, lift up the left toes, with left sole as axis, turn body leftward 180 degrees, stretch both arms forward, posture in the left bow stance and accompanied by exhalation (Figure. 24-5).

2. With the left second finger pointing at the right second finger tip, practise as above firstly moving the Qi along the Right Large Intestine Meridian; secondly with the left second finger pointing at the right small finger, practise as above moving the Qi along the Right Small Intestine Meridian; thirdly with the left second finger pointing at the right fourth finger, practise as above moving the Qi along the Right Triple Warmer Meridian (Figures. 24-5 (1) (2) (3), 24-6).

FUNCTIONS:

This step can improve the physiological functions of the three Yang meridians of the arms, regulate the functions of the digestive, assimilative and excretory organs. In addition it can smoothen the flow of Qi and blood in the upper limbs and improve the function of the cervical vertebrae. It is good for the prevention and cure of periarthritis of the shoulder, problems of the neck vertebrae, chronic enteritis and habitual constipation.

Fig.24-5

Fig.24-6

129

STEP 25: THE THREE YANG MERIDIANS OF THE LEFT AND RIGHT LEGS (TRAVELLING FROM HEAD TO FEET)

References as in Step 23.

THEORY:

In addition to having the three Yin meridians and three Yang meridians in the arms, the body also has three Yin meridians and three Yang meridians in the legs. The "Three Yang of Legs" refers to the Stomach Meridian, the Urinary Bladder Meridian and the Gall Bladder Meridian. They all travel from the head to the feet. The first Yang is the Yangming Stomach Meridian of the Leg, travelling from the eyes along the front of the body down to the second toe. The second Yang is the Taiyang Urinary Bladder Meridian of the Leg, travelling from the inner corner of the eye to the tip of the fifth toe along the back of the body. The third Yang is the Shaoyang Gall Bladder Meridian of the Leg, travelling from the outer corner of the eye to the tip of the fourth toe along the side of the body. The practice of the Three Yang Meridians of the Legs together with the moving of the Qi along the meridians has positive results in smoothening the Qi flow along the Stomach, the Urinary Bladder and the Gall Bladder Meridians and also in tuning up the functions of the various organs and bowels.

This step calls for totally internal concentration, i.e. with the hand assisting the will (Yi), the Yi leading the Qi, guiding along the meridians to regulate the mind, breathing and energy. If one can remember some important acupoints during the practice the effects are so much better, the thinking and memory abilities can be increased.

The first Yang is the Stomach Meridian of Foot-Yanming, the first point of this meridian is Chengqi (S. 1); Lidui (S. 45) is the terminal point.

The second Yang is the Urinary Bladder Meridian of Foot-Taiyang, the first point of this meridian is Jingming (B. 1); Zhiyin (B. 67) is the terminal point.

The third Yang is the Gall Bladder Meridian of Foot-Shaoyang, the first point of this meridian is Tong-ziliao (G. 1); Zuqiaoyin (G. 44) is the terminal point.

1 Chengqi (S. 1): Between the eyeball and the mid-point of the infra-orbital ridge.

2 Lidui (S. 45): On the lateral side of the second toe, about 0.1 *cun* behind the corner of nail.

3 Jingming (B. 1): Just 0.1 *cun* above the inner canthus.

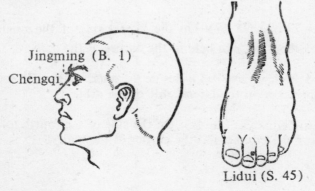

Jingming (B. 1)

Chengqi

Lidui (S. 45)

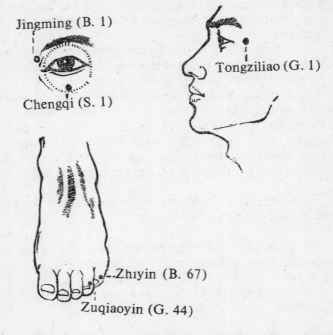

Jingming (B. 1)

Tongziliao (G. 1)

Chengqi (S. 1)

Zhiyin (B. 67)

Zuqiaoyin (G. 44)

4 Zhiyin (B. 67): On the lateral side of the small toe, about 0.1 *cun* behind the corner of the nail.

5 Tongziliao (G. 1): Beside the outer canthus, in the depression on the lateral side of the orbit.

6 Zuqiaoyin (G. 44): On the side of the fourth toe, about 0.1 *cun* behind the corner of the nail.

Fig.25-1

METHOD:

1. Firstly moving the Qi along the Stomach Meridian: From the last movement, shift the body weight backward while moving the Qi to Dazhui (Du 14) along the right Triple Warmer Meridian, turn the right foot outward 90 degrees followed by making a step in front, both arms gradually raise along the sides high up from the back accompanying by inhalation (Figure. 25-1). Next slowly lower both arms, palms facing in-

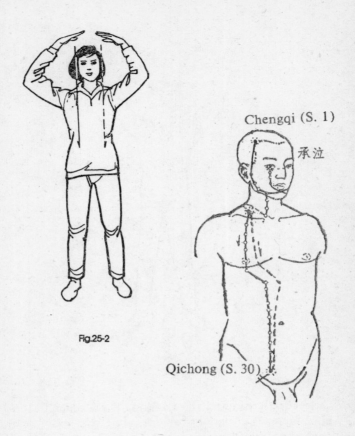

Chengqi (S. 1)
承泣

Fig.25-2

Qichong (S. 30)

ward, move the Qi following the Stomach Meridian along the chest and abdomen to the second and third toes accompanying by exhalation (Figures 25-2, 3).

134

Fig.25-3

厉兑
(Lidui S. 45)

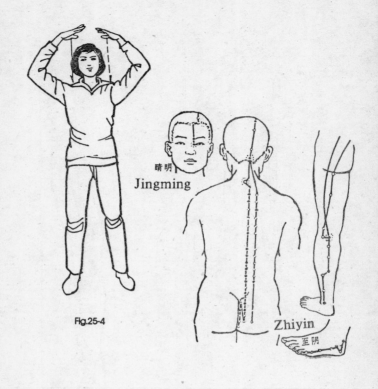

Fig.25-4

Jingming

睛明

Zhiyin

至阴

2. Secondly moving the Qi along the Urinary Bladder: From the last movement, rotate both arms outward, palms facing up and raise high up along the body sides accompanying by inhalation (Figure. 25-4). Turn

136

Fig.25-5

the palms and move the Qi along the Urinary Bladder Meridian (back of the body), moving from up to down through the top of the head, back of the neck, and then both pass arms through the armpits and push down the palms (Figure. 25-5), palms facing back and while reaching the back of the tights turn the palms to face inward, the concentration continues to move the Qi down to the tips of the small toes accompanying by exhalation.

137

Fig.25-6

3. Thirdly moving the Qi along the Gall Bladder Meridian: From the last movement, extend both arms, raise high up gradually and accompanied by inhalation (Figure. 25-6). Turn palms and move the Qi following

Fig.25-7

the Gall Bladder Meridian (along body sides), down-ward from the sides of the head through the armpits to the ribs to reach the tips of the fourth toes accompany-ing by exhalation (Figures. 25-7, 8).

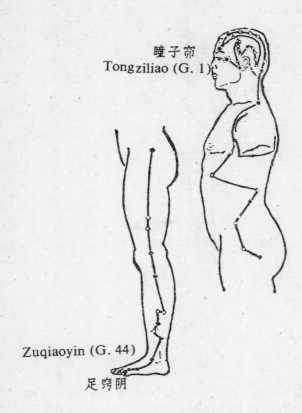

瞳子髎
Tongziliao (G. 1)

Zuqiaoyin (G. 44)
足窍阴

Fig.25-8

FUNCTIONS:

This step can strengthen the physiological functions of the Stomach, the Urinary Bladder and the Gall Bladder Meridians. It has useful therapeutic effects for anorexia, abdominal distention, borborygmus, malfunctioning of the vegetative nervous system, fullness in the chest and hypochondrium, insomnia, dreaminess and hypertension.

STEP 26: THE THREE YIN MERIDIANS OF THE LEFT AND RIGHT LEGS (TRAVELLING FROM FEET TO HEAD)

References as in Step 23.

THEORY:

This step calls for internal concentration only, i.e. with the hand assisting the will (Yi), the Yi leading the Qi, guiding along the meridians so as to regulate the mind, breathing and energy. It makes use of the concentration to regulate the physiological functions of the Three Yin Meridians of the Legs.

The "Three Yin of the Legs" means that there are also three Yin meridians in the legs; these are the Spleen Meridian, the Kidney Meridian and the Liver Meridian. These three meridians all move from the feet upward to the head. The first Yin is the Taiyin Spleen Meridian of the Leg, travelling upward from the side of the big toe along the outer side of the breast, turning back to below the armpit and moving up to the mouth and lips; the second Yin is the Shaoyin Kidney Meridian of the Leg, travelling upward from the center of the foot through the inner side of the collar bone and moving up to the ear. The third Yin Meridian is the Jueyin Liver Meridian of the Leg, travelling upward from the tip of the big toe to the bottom of the breast and reaches upward to the eye.

If one can remember some important acupoints during the practice the effects are so much better, the thinking and memory abilities can be increased.

The first Ying is the Spleen Meridian of the Foot-

Taiyin, the first point of this meridian is Yinbai (Sp. 1); Dabao (Sp. 21) is the terminal point.

The second Yin is the Kidney Meridian of Foot-Shaoyin, the first point of this meridian is Yongquan (K. 1); Shufu (K. 27) is the terminal point.

The third Yin is the Liver Meridian of Foot-Jueyin, the first point of this meridian is Dadun (Liv. 1); Qimen (Liv. 14) is the terminal point.

1 Yinbai (Sp. 1): On the medial side of the big toe, about 0.1 *cun* posterior to the corner of the nail.

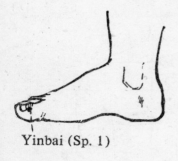

Yinbai (Sp. 1)

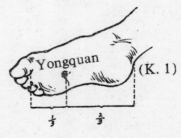

Yongquan (K. 1)

$\frac{1}{3}$ $\frac{2}{3}$

2 Dabao (Sp. 21): On the mid-axillary line, 6 *cun* below the axilla, midway between the axilla and free end of the eleventh rib.

3 Yongquan (K. 1): In the depression appearing on the sole when the foot is in plantar flection, approximately at the junction of the front and middle thirds of the sole.

4 Shufu (K. 27): In the depression on the lower border of the clavicle, 2 *cun* to the side of the Ren Meridian.

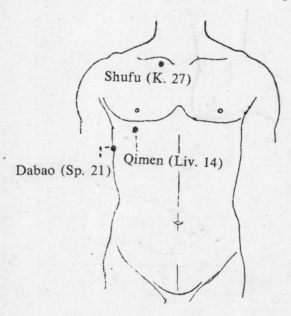

5 Dadun (Liv. 1): On the side of the dorsum of the terminal phalanx of the big toe, between the lateral corner of the nail and interphalangeal joint.

6 Qimen (Liv. 14): On the mammillary line, two ribs below the nipple, in the sixth intercostal space.

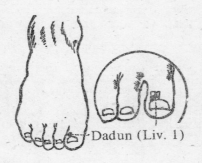

Dadun (Liv. 1)

METHOD:

A. THE THREE YIN MERIDIANS OF THE LEFT LEG

1. Firstly moving the Qi along the Left Spleen Meridian: From the last movement, gradually turn the body leftward, turn right toes leftward 45 degrees and left toes leftward 90 degrees, raise the left arm, lift up

Fig.26-1

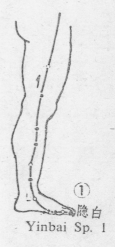

隐白
Yinbai Sp. 1

the left leg, and meanwhile stretch the right arm, with
right "sword fingers" pointing the will (Yi) at the tip
of the left big toe (Figure. 26-1 (1)). Next move the Qi,
along the Spleen Meridian, i.e. right sword fingers
move from the outer side of the big toe upward to the

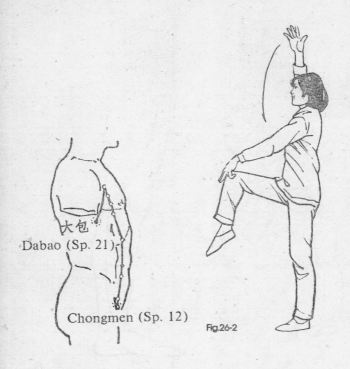

大包
Dabao (Sp. 21)

Chongmen (Sp. 12)

Fig.26-2

back of the knee, move the left leg slowly a step backward, the right hand continues to move up through the chest and hypochondrium accompanying by inhalation, then through the front of armpit and moves to below the armpit while turning the body leftward slowly and accompanied by exhalation.

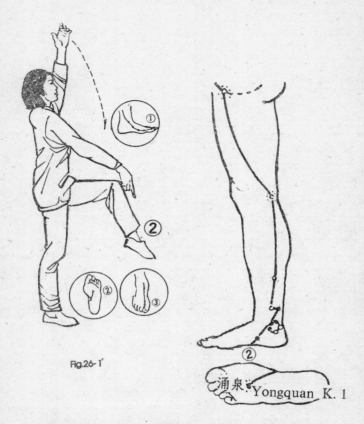

Fig.26-1'

涌泉 Yongquan K. 1

2. Secondly moving the Qi along the Left Kidney Meridian: From the last movement, gradually lower the left arm and meanwhile raise the right arm, lift up the right leg and accompanied by inhalation (Figure. 26-1 (2)). Next move the right foot one step forward, body weight on the right foot accompanying by exhal-

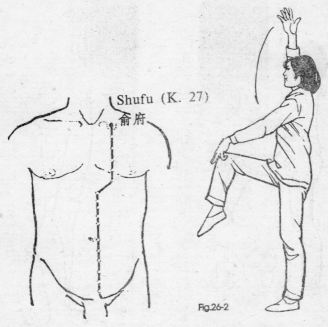

Shufu (K. 27)
俞府

Fig.26-2

ation. Raise the left arm again, lift up the left leg, right sword fingers pointing at the center of the left foot accompanying by inhalation (refer to Figure. 26-1), following this, move the Qi along the Kidney Meridian, up to the back of the knee joints, move the left leg one step backward accompanying by exhalation, right fingers reach the inner side of the left collar bone along the abdomen and chest, continue to raise the right arm high up and lift up the right leg accompanying by inhalation. Next move the right leg forward one step accompanying by exhalation. Raise the left arm again,

149

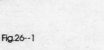

Fig.26--1

lift the left leg, right sword fingers pointing at the outer side of the big toe accompanying by inhalation (refer to Figure. 26-1 (3)).

3. Thirdly moving the Qi along the Left Liver Meridian: From the last movement, as the above procedures move the Qi along the Liver Meridian, the right

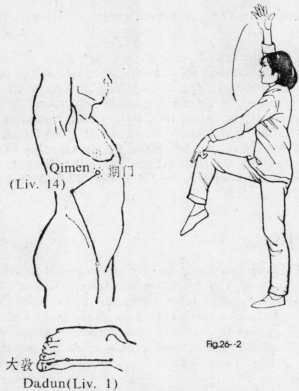

Qimen
(Liv. 14)

期门

大敦

Dadun(Liv. 1)

Fig.26--2

sword fingers passing through the back of the left knee joint, move the left leg one step backward, move up right fingers again by passing around the sex organ to reach the chest and hypochondrium and continue to raise high up, slowly lower the left arm and meanwhile lift up the left leg accompanying by inhalation (refer to Figure. 26-1 (3)).

B. THE THREE YIN MERIDIANS OF THE RIGHT FOOT

From the last movement, hold left hand in sword finger posture and point at the inner side of the right big toe, following the above procedures move the Qi along the right Spleen Meridian; left sword fingers pointing at the center of the right foot, move the Qi along the right Kidney Meridian as the procedures outlined above; the left sword fingers pointing to the outer side of the right big toe, move the Qi along the right Liver Meridian as the above method (Figure. 26-2).

FUNCTIONS:

This step can strengthen the physiological functions of the three Yin Meridians of Spleen, Kidney and Liver. The spleen takes charge of assimilation and controls the blood; the kidney stores the essence of life (reproductive essence and food essence) and controls the discharge of urine and stool, regulate the metabolism of body fluid and the functioning of the internal secretion; the liver stores blood, controls the emotion, regulates the menses and brightens the eyes. Hence by practising this step along the meridians the flow of Qi in the meridians can be smoothened and the blood and Qi can be regulated. It definitely has therapeutic effects for the prevention and cure of indigestion, weakness of the spleen and stomach, over-exertion and deficiency of the spleen and kidney, general edema and insomnia, bad emotion and irritability, irregular menstruation, weakening of sexual ability and general weakness and lethargy.

STEP 27: BOUNCING A BALL WHILE STEPPING

THEORY:

The external concentration is "bouncing a ball while stepping" and the internal concentration is at Laogong (P 8) in the middle of the palms.

This is the stabilising step after the "leg three Yin step" (Step 26). The concentration is on the right hand Laogong to exert force in bouncing the ball while lifting the left leg but the concentration is on the left hand Laogong to bounce the ball with force while lifting the right leg. These movements are used to regulate the mind, breathing and energy, to balance and regulate the physiology functions of the left and right cerebral hemispheres to improve the co-ordinating functions of the cerebrum.

Fig.27-1

METHOD:

1. From the above movement, shift the body weight backward when the left hand moves along the Liver Meridian to the inner portion of the right collar bone, turn the left toes inward 90 degrees, shift the body weight to left leg, gradually raise both arms high upward from the back accompanying by inhalation (Figure. 27-1). Retract right leg to shoulder width and the

Fig.27-2

body weight is now in the centre between both legs.
Slowly lower both arms and place them at the sides
accompanying by exhalation (Figure. 27-2).

Fig.27-3

2. Shift body weight to the right leg, lift up the left leg and meanwhile raise the right arm in front of right shoulder and accompanied by inhalation (Figure. 27-3). Next with will power, exert force in the right hand Laogong to bounce the ball and meanwhile step down the left foot accompanying by exhalation process during the movement.

Fig.27-4

3. Shift body weight to left leg, lift up right leg and meanwhile raise the left arm in front of left shoulder accompanying by inhalation (Figure. 27-4). Next bounce the ball with the left hand while stepping down the right foot accompanying by exhalation.

The above left and right movement is considered as one time, repeat 3—5 times.

FUNCTIONS:

The alternating left and right co-ordinated movements can improve the regulatory function of the cerebrum, improve the Qi and blood circulation and smoothen the joints. Hence this step has definite effects for prevention and cure of cerebrovascular disease, shoulder periarthritis, and in improving the functions of joints.

STEP 28: REGULATING QI IN REN AND DU MERIDIANS

Refernces as in Step-23.

THEORY:

This step requires totally internal concentration, i.e. with the hands assisting the Yi (will), with Yi leading the Qi (vital force) to regulate the mind, breathing and energy along the meridians. With concentration guide the Ren and Du meridians of the small circle of Qi in order to regulate, improve and strengthen the balancing function between the two meridians.

The Ren and Du meridians belong to the group of eight extra meridians. The ancient word of "Ren" was the same as the word for "pregnancy" and hence it is closely related to reproduction. It controls all the Yin meridians of the body and the Ren meridian is also known as "the ocean of all the Yin". It originates from Dantian, emerges through Huiyin (Ren. 1), ascends through the front middle line, goes around the lips and reaches to the areas below the eyes. "Du" means governor and commander. Du meridian governs all the Yang of the body and is also known as "the ocean of all Yang". It originates from Dantian and emerges from Huiyin (Ren. 1), ascends along the back middle line and moves along the inside of spine to the brain, around the mouth and connects to the Ren meridian to form a "small circle of Qi" and this is also known as "connecting the Ren and Du meridians".

The first point of the Ren Meridian is Huiyin (R. 1); Chengjian (R. 24) is the terminal point. ·

The first point of the Du Meridian is Changqiang (D. 1); Yinjiao (D. 28) is the terminal point.

1 Huiyin (R. 1): At the center of the perineum. It lies between the anus and the scrotum in males and between the anus and the posterior labial commissure in females.

2 Chengjian (R. 24): In the depression at the center of the mentolabial groove.

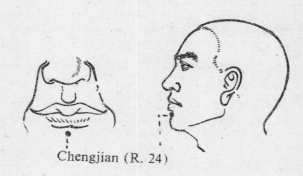

Chengjian (R. 24)

Huiyin (R. 1)

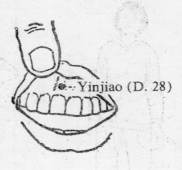

Yinjiao (D. 28)

Changqiang (D. 1)

3 Changqiang (D. 1): Midway between the tip of the coccyx and the anus. Locate the point in a prone position.

4 Yinjiao (D. 28): Between the upper lip and the upper labial gingiva, in the frenulum of the upper lip.

METHOD:

Fig.28-1   Fig.28-2

1. From the above movement, change both hands to palms with palms facing down, extend and point the fingers outside (Figure. 28-1). Next turn palms to face up with concentration at the fingers pointing toward Huiyin (Ren. 1). For those who are deficient in Yin and excessive in Yang, lead the Qi to travel from Huiyin upward along the front middle line (Ren meridian) to reach Baihui (Du 20) through the mouth and eyes (Figure. 28-2). Now lift both arms together high up with the concentration to place above the Baihui (Du 20), palms facing down and accompanied by inhalation (Figure. 28-2). Next fill body with the Qi while

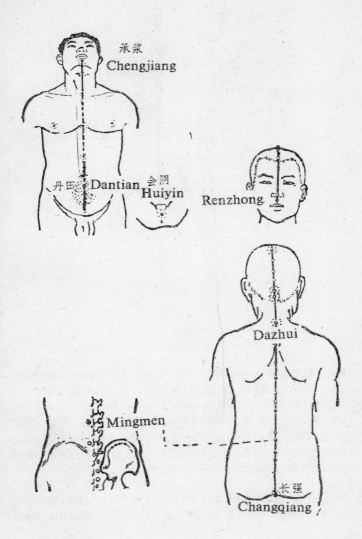

承浆
Chengjiang

丹田 Dantian　会阴
Huiyin　Renzhong

Dazhui

Mingmen

长强
Changqiang

Fig.28-3

both hands are gradually lowering but the concentration travels from Baihui (Du 20) to Huiyin (Ren. 1) along the back middle line through Mingmen (Du 4) accompanying by exhalation (Figure. 28-3). This form of practice is to raise the Yin and to lower the Yang and is suitable for hyperactivity of liver-Yang such as those who suffer from hypertension.

2. For those who are deficient in Yang and excessive in Yin, lead the Qi to Baihui (Du 20) along the back

Fig.28-4

middle line (Du meridian) through Mingmen (Du 4), lift both arms together high up with concentration and place above Baihui (Du 20) with the palms changed to facing down. The movement is as above but the concentration differs. Next pass the concentration through the eyes and mouth and gradually lower down along the front middle line accompanying by exhalation (Figure. 28-4). Fill the Qi at Huiyin (Ren 1). This method of practice is to lower Yang and to raise Yin and is suitable for those who suffer from illness due to Yang deficiency and excessive Yin. These include hypothyrosis, feeling cold in the body and those who are deficient in Yang and those with low metabolism while suffering chronic diseases.

3. For those who are healthy and balance in Yin and Yang, regulate the Qi of Ren and Du meridians along the middle line (the passageway of Jing Qi), which is referred to the length between Huiyin and Baihui. While practising usually one can feel the Qi sensation moving through the passageway.

The above raising up and lowering down is considered as one time, repeat 3—5 times.

FUNCTIONS:

This step can strengthen the self regulating functions of both the Ren and Du meridians and it further helps in maintaining the co-ordination of the Yin and Yang of the whole body. This is the healthy state of "harmonious balance of Yin and Yang" and "balanced control of spirit and mind". This step thus has good therapeutic effects in the prevention and cure of hypertension, disorder of the nervous system functions and menopausal syndrome.

CONCLUSION STEP

The conclusion step is the requirement for the whole body to relax and for the Qi to sink into Dantian toward the end of the practice. The ancient texts state that "kidney is the origin of congenital constitution" (i.e. the kidney essence is the foundation of reproduction and development of life) and that "kidney should

Fig.28-5

not be subjected to purgation or reduction". Hence
before conclusion one should willfully lead the Qi with
concentration, and do the conclusion after "lifting the
Qi of kidney" so as to avoid any possible undesirable
effect arising from the practice. The practice of conclusion step is as follows:

Pile up the Laogong of both hands and place at the
Dantian (extra). For males, the left hand at the inside
while for females the right hand at the inside, lift the
kidney Qi 3—5 times (Figure. 28-5). (This is to lift up

Fig.28-6　　　Fig.28-7

reproductive organ, contract the anus and meanwhile bite the teeth, practise 3—5 times.) The kidney Qi takes charge of both the reproductive organ and the anus, kidney also takes charge of bone and it stores the Jing (essence of life) and this is the socalled "lifting the kidney Qi". Next lift up the soles and then gradually relax and lower to the ground to conclude (Figures. 28-6, 7).

ACKNOWLEDGMENT FROM THE TRANSLATOR

I wish to thank my Master, Professor Li Ding for teaching me the art of Taiji Qigong Twenty-Eight Step and for his kind request for me to carry out the translation. Without his dedicated teaching, I will not know the art, without his request I will not have the honour to translate. A master is to be respected for life and an honour is to be appreciated and acknowledged.

Here I would also like to express my sincere thanks and gratitude to Mr. T. T Ang, President of Singapore Acupuncture Society and Principal of Chinese Nature-Cure Institute, Singapore for his advice and encouragement to undertake the translation. I must also thank Mr. Ang for providing me the opportunity to learn the art of Taiji Qigong Twenty-Eight Steps from Professor Li Ding.

FLINGOH C. H. OH
18 June, 1988
Dragon Boat Festival
Kuala Lumpur

Traditional Chinese Therapeutic Exercises and Techniques

Atlas of Therapeutic Motion for Treatment and Health
—A Guide to Traditional Chinese Massage and
Exercise Therapy

Traditional Chinese Therapeutic Exercises and Techniques
Standing Pole

Chinese Single Broadsword
A Primer of Basic Skills and Performance Routines for
Practitioners

Sinew-Transforming Exercises

Pediatric *Tuina* **Therapy**

Eating Your Way to Health
Diet Therapy in Traditional Chinese Medicine

Keep Fit the Chinese Way

Meridian Qigong

Taiji Qigong
Twenty-Eight Steps